I only said it didn't hurt

Dr. Celia Banting

WIGHITA PRESS

Wighita Press
P.O. Box 30399
Little Rock, Arkansas 72260-0399

www.wighitapress.com

This is a work of fiction. Names of characters, places, and incidents are products of the author's imagination and are used fictitiously and are not to be construed as real. Any resemblance to actual events, locales, organizations, or persons, living or dead, is purely coincidental.

Library of Congress Cataloging-in-Publication Data

Banting, Celia
I Only Said It Didn't Hurt/Dr. Celia Banting – 1st Edition
p. cm.
ISBN 9780978664862 (paperback)

1. Therapeutic novel 2. Cutting 3. Self-harm 4. Suicide prevention

Library of Congress Control Number: 2007930367

Layout by Michelle VanGeest
Cover production by Luke Johnson

Printed by Dickinson Press, Grand Rapids, Michigan, USA

Issues addressed in this book:

Inter-generational behavioral patterns
Care-giver roles
Cutting and self-harm
Personality development
Five parts of the self
Taking control of the self
Corresponding behaviors
Assimilated Injunctions
Innate nurturing
Attention seeking behavior
Raising self-esteem
Maintaining safe boundaries
Effective communication
Stress management
Self-soothing
Achieving true intimacy

Dedicated to Erica Elsie and to precious Destiny for her courage and faith in trying this therapy in order to change her own destiny. Also dedicated to sweet Lauren for her enduring pursuit of romance.

Acknowledgments

My grateful thanks go to my proofreader and typesetter, Michelle VanGeest, who frees me from my dyslexic brain, and replaces my mother's voice. Thanks to Bev, my stray-word spotter, too. I thank my wonderful husband, Des, for the inspiration and support he gives me. Thank you to Luke and Sam for their faith, inspiration and talent. Thank you to Helen and Dave, and Moya and Tony for their faith and support—and especially Moya who introduced me to Beringuer newborn dolls and the world of "reborning." Thank you to Susan Harring and Ron Woldyk for their reliability and professionalism. Thank you to my dear friend Vicki for her guiding sense of style.

Thank you to all my psychotherapy tutors and colleagues at the Metanoia Institute, London, for teaching me about human nature, psychopathology, growth and recovery. My utmost respect goes to the late Dr. Eric Berne, and all the innovative thinkers who came after him, and hope that he would approve of the re-labeling of his ego states to help clarify his theory in order to help teenagers who just didn't "get it."

Thank you to Mr. Philip Pullman, author of *The Golden Compass,* for kindly agreeing to allow me to use his concept of an externalized soul for therapeutic purposes.

I thank the good Lord for giving me a lively imagination, and I also thank my parents for moving to the Isle of Wight, "the land that bobs in and out of view, depending upon the sea mist."

Chapter One

"**D**on't be such a baby, Marsha," Dad snaps at me. "You're fifteen, for heaven sake."

I don't dare answer back. I learned my lesson years ago when I was little. Why does he have to be so mean?

"You'll be okay, honey," a nurse says. "Here's something for the pain."

She injects something into the needle strapped to my hand and passes me a tissue. I wipe my nose clumsily with my free hand.

"Appendicitis is *very* painful, sir. She is not being a baby."

I give her a bleak smile for sticking up for me.

Dad glares at her and waits until she walks away before letting me know what he thinks again.

"Well, tears are for babies. My father used to tell me..." *Here we go,* I think to myself, "...how his men suffered dreadful injuries and never so much as squeaked."

I'm so sick of hearing about his father, my grandfather. I know I shouldn't think like that, and I should be grateful for the sacrifices his generation made for us. I *am*; I'm just tired of having Dad go on and on about it every minute of the day.

I don't know how long my grandfather was in the military; I kind of tune out when Dad starts on about it. But I know that he told Dad story after story, in the same way I'm expected to read fairytales to my little brother and sister, Casey and Shelley. It doesn't matter what anyone's talking about, it'll get Dad started, and he'll say, "Oh, that reminds me of something my father told me," and off he'll go.

"...One bomb blew his leg off," he says. "Are you listening to me?"

"Sorry, Dad," I wince with pain. "I feel dizzy. I think the medicine's kicking in."

He looks irritated with me but I close my eyes, thankful that the edges of the biting pain in my stomach are blurring as he speaks. His voice blends into the sounds of the hospital beyond my bed, and I drift away.

Fragmented thoughts float into my mind. Where's Mom? It hurts that she couldn't be bothered to come to the hospital with me. Too drunk, I guess. Who's going to look after Casey and Shelley without me there? Mom won't bother and Dad's too busy. But as the thoughts blend together, I drift further away and everything goes black.

• • • •

I wake up with someone squeezing my finger so hard that I gasp.

"Good girl, breathe! There you go."

I choke as something is pulled out of my throat, and as a feeling of panic threatens to suffocate me, I suck in air, panting. I don't know where I am. My world is just six inches from my face. It's filled with someone shaking me, and telling me to breathe deeply.

I can hear alarm bells going off. I gasp for breath like someone drowning, and the alarm bells stop.

"Good girl. Good job. She's fine," I hear someone say, and I'm aware that whoever was by my bed has gone.

Time floats in and out of my consciousness, and it doesn't really settle on me until my stomach rumbles. It's time for food.

I wake up in a ward that has another person in it, who is snoring. I try to sit up, but a sharp pain shoots through me, and I flop back down, whimpering. I don't like this. I want it to go away.

A nurse comes towards me with a flashlight. It must be nighttime. Dad's not by my bed, but I'm not surprised.

"Are you okay?" she asks.

"I think so. Where am I?"

"You've had your operation and everything went well. You're fine. You just need to recover, that's all."

"I'm hungry," I venture.

"D'you feel sick?" she asks.

I feel woozy, but I don't feel sick.

"No."

She walks away and comes back with a plate of buttered toast. She helps me to sit up. I wince, as the pain is awful. I have tears in my eyes. If I weren't so hungry, I wouldn't have bothered moving.

Every mouthful is wonderful, and when I'm done, I slip back down into the bed and fall asleep.

• • • •

I'm home within days and back to my old routine, taking care of Mom, Casey and Shelley, and dodging Dad's military stories, telling me how thankful I should be.

I limp around the house, my stomach cramping in pain, trying to do my chores. Mom's on the couch, drunk, and the kids are outside in the yard. Dad's out.

It's a weird thing. You would think that if your dad gets onto you enough about how cool the military is, then one day you'd want to experience it yourself, but it wasn't like that with my dad. Even though he talked about it all the time, he had never joined up. Dad's mom, my Granny, said that he had "flat feet," whatever that meant, and was rejected.

Mom told me that he'd tried to join the National Guard several times, but he was always rejected. But Dad wasn't deterred; he lived out his military life in our home and backyard. He had Casey marching up and down the path with a broomstick sticking up over his shoulder.

"Attention!" he would shout, and Casey would come to a stop abruptly. And with a squeaky six-year-old voice, he would shout, "Sir! Yes, sir!"

Sometimes when Casey got his steps wrong, Dad would yell at him and he'd cry. "Stop crying," Dad would shout. "Boys don't cry. By the left, quick march," and Casey would sniff, as he started to march up and down the path again. "Left, left, left right left."

I felt sorry for him, but I didn't say anything. I was just glad that Dad wasn't picking on me.

Everything changed for Casey when Dad got a letter from the National Guard, saying that he'd been accepted because the situation in Iraq was getting worse, and the government needed more men.

I hear him singing in the bathroom as he gets ready to leave. He's glad to go, having waited so long to live the life his father has talked about.

I know that Casey is glad Dad's going; Shelley is

too, but Mom cries and cries.

As he heads for the door, Dad says, "Lillian, stop it. You know I can't handle seeing you cry. Stop it. You've got Marsha here to help you. Get control of yourself, for pity sake."

Mom drapes herself around him as he opens the door, and he pries her hands off him as he steps outside. He doesn't kiss her, or wave, as he walks down the path, and he totally ignores me.

"Bye," I say, feeling nothing. "Come inside, Mom."

"Leave me alone," she snaps at me, as she heads towards the liquor cabinet.

Well, excuse me, I think, going to my room.

I turn my music up loud to drown out her wailing downstairs, and I watch the kids outside, playing quietly in the yard. From my window I can see the neighbors' kids yelling and screaming in their yard, and it strikes me how quiet my brother and sister are compared to them.

I guess I'm quiet, too. The kids at school say I am, and sometimes I hear them call me a loner. I don't know why it is. I like people and I'm nice to them, or I think I am, but I just don't have anything to say to anyone. It's hard to feel excited about the things they do. In fact, now that I think about it, I rarely feel anything at all. Most of the time I feel numb, and I have felt that way for ages.

Ever since I can remember, I wasn't allowed to

show any feelings. Even when I felt angry because Dad picked on me and Mom expected me to do everything when she was drunk, I wasn't allowed to show my feelings. No one told me that, but it's just something I knew inside; it was like a silent rule in our family.

When I was little, Granddad would shout at me. He'd say, "Children should be seen and not heard," and if I ever cried, he looked at me as if I were something disgusting. He'd tell Dad to give me something to cry about.

Dad would stand over me and say, "You can quit that nonsense; it won't work with me, so you may as well go to your room. You can come out when you quit being such a baby."

"You tell her," Granddad would say.

I always knew that Granddad didn't like Mom. I heard him saying bad things about her once, when he didn't know I was listening.

"Why d'you put up with her nonsense, son? Be the man of the house. If she were my wife, I'd put her in her place. I can't stand people who can't control themselves; they're so weak."

It's true that Mom couldn't control the way she felt; she was always crying and getting hysterical. Dad shouted at her all the time, and I decided that I was never going to be like her. I wasn't going to show my feelings like she did. I didn't have to worry, though, because I didn't seem to *have* any feelings.

Mom's parents lived so far away that we rarely saw them. Dad never actually said bad things about them, but I could tell that he didn't like them. When Granddad came to stay, I heard him ask about them and say, "It's just as well," when Dad said that they couldn't afford to travel.

Granny seemed to stick up for Mom's parents, though.

"Perhaps Lillian would be more, um, *stable* if her parents were nearer and able to help her."

Granddad sounded just like Dad. "Don't be stupid, woman, where d'you think she learned how to be so *useless*? Oh, sorry, son," he added as an afterthought.

I'd crept back to my room feeling confused. Mom had told me over and over how she and Dad met. It had been my favorite story when I was little, and she was sober. She'd make Dad sound like a hero, and she was his princess.

"He was so stiff, so upright and proper; so different than me," she would giggle. "I think I confused him. He called me his 'little butterfly' because I would flit about. Sometimes he'd scratch his head when I slid down the slide on a kids' playground, as if he couldn't quite figure me out. But he seemed to want what I had, and I forced him to climb to the top of the slide and slip down after me. He'd laughed and said that he'd never had so much fun.

You should have seen me in my wedding dress; I was like a fairy princess."

She'd show me photos of them on their wedding day, and I knew that everything she'd told me was true. Dad stood there, stiff, rigid and proper, while she clung onto his arm with her leg bent up behind her, pulling a goofy face. The family photo showed Dad's parents standing there as rigid as he was, and Mom's parents laughing, dressed in wild clothes.

I grew up not knowing Mom's parents, as Mom and Dad had moved soon after they got married to live nearer to Dad's parents. I was born ten months later.

When I look at Mom as she is now, she's nothing like the person she was in her wedding pictures. I don't know what's happened to her. Maybe it's the alcohol. I don't know.

I shake my thoughts from my head, and I see Casey and Shelley sitting quietly in the garden, ignoring the noisy kids next door. I guess all three of us are quiet, not a bit like Mom, who is *very* noisy.

Mom hammers on my door.

"Turn that racket off," she says, and I hear her dissolve into tears. "What about my nerves? Don't you care about me at all? My husband's just gone off to fight overseas, and all you can do is make my headache worse."

I don't open the door because I don't want to see her drunken face, begging me to make things better for her. I can't cope with her when she's like this, so I turn my music off and throw myself on my bed. I try to ignore the sounds of her sobbing as she goes down the stairs.

My heart races. She makes me feel guilty. Thanks to me, she's more upset than she was when Dad left half an hour ago. Something inside me festers, as I hear the neighbor's kids laughing and being loud. My brother and sister are in the yard, still quiet, and I'm lying here on my bed, robbed of my music because Mom has a headache. It doesn't seem fair somehow.

I fall asleep listening to the sounds from our neighbor's garden and only awake when there's a knock on my door.

"Marsha, wake up. We're hungry."

I glance at the clock on my bedside cabinet. Heck, I've been asleep for two hours. I've got to get dinner.

I get up and open the door. The kids come into my room.

Shelley looks anxious. "Mom's sick," she says.

I know what that means. She's not sick at all. She's drunk.

The look on their little faces turns my stomach. They didn't ask to have such crappy parents, so I put on a happy face to hide the emptiness inside me and tell them to follow me downstairs.

Mom's on the sofa watching her soaps. "Shut up,

I can't hear," she snaps, when I ask the kids what they want for dinner. I feel my jaw tense. I lower my voice and ask them again. They say, "Fries."

I know that I'll get into trouble if I don't make Mom something to eat, so I go over to her and ask her what she wants.

She looks at me as if she's seeing me for the first time, as if I'm a total stranger in her house.

"Um, what?" Then she grabs me by the wrist. "I'm hungry. My husband's left me. You'd be upset if it happened to you."

I try to bite my tongue, but I can't. "Dad hasn't left you; he's gone overseas to fight." But as I say it, I can't help but think that she's got it right and I've got it wrong. Dad was desperate to leave, and he didn't even give us a second glance as he hurried off to fulfill his dream.

I pull my hand away and stand tall.

"What d'you want to eat?" I ask her again, showing no emotion at all.

She sobs. "You're so like your father," she cries. "So cold."

Great! Thanks!

"So, what d'you want to eat?"

She sits up, groaning loudly, and suddenly she looks like an actor on a stage, but one that's awful — the sort who's told not to give up their day job.

"Oh, I feel so ill," she says, wiping her brow. "I can only manage something small."

But as usual, she eats everything I give her, and that's a lot. I want her to fall asleep, because only then will she give me a break.

Finally she's asleep on the couch and it's quieter. We're quiet, as we don't want to wake her. Even though Casey and Shelley are only little, they've learned to be quiet around Mom.

The three of us sit in the kitchen, munching fries, dipping them into tomato sauce. They're good, and I'm starving. I haven't bothered to cook much to-night, as Dad's not here. Normally he'd want a full meal, the type his father used to get when he was in the military — wholesome food — but I didn't have time tonight. The kids don't mind, though; they're happy that Dad's not here forcing them to eat their vegetables.

The house seems different in the morning with-out Dad barking at us to get ready or we'll be late. "You know how I hate tardiness," he'd say. I get the kids up and give them cereal, and we leave the house at the same time that we would have, had Dad been here nagging us. I don't bother to say goodbye to Mom, because she's still in bed, sleeping off a hangover.

As the days turn into weeks, every morning's the same. I get the kids up and off to school, and Mom's in bed, oblivious to the three of us in the house. When school finishes, I pick up Casey and Shelley and we trek home again.

One day Mom's on the couch with the television blaring. She's holding a letter in her hands, and she's crying.

"What's the matter?" I ask.

She looks more lost than usual.

"Mom's coming to stay. My dad's left her," and suddenly out of nowhere, she screams at me, "Get this place cleaned up."

The kids look scared and go out into the backyard. I grit my teeth, wanting to yell back, but I know it'll do no good when she's this way.

I dump my schoolbag down and start picking stuff up.

"Don't touch that," Mom yells. "I want that next to me. What's wrong with you? Pick up the mess, not my magazines."

She starts crying all over again, and I feel locked in a place where it's okay for her to pick on me but, because she's in pieces, I can't stick up for myself. There's a festering resentment growing inside me with nowhere to go. I can't let it out, for if I did, Mom would take it out on the three of us.

There's junk everywhere. Since Dad left, no one's cleaned the house and it's a pigsty. I've coped with getting the kids and myself to school, feeding us all, and doing laundry, but I haven't had time to clean up. As I look around me, I don't know where to begin.

Part of me wishes that the kids were older and

could help me, but right now I'm glad they're out-side, away from Mom's hysteria.

"I hope there are clean sheets," Mom frets. "Go and check, will you?"

I stop picking up Mom's dirty plates that are all around the couch, and I go upstairs to look in the linen closet.

"Make up the spare bed in your room," she calls up the stairs.

This time I answer back. "What? No! She can't stay in my room."

Mom bursts into tears again and corners me by breaking down.

"Why are you arguing with me? Are you deter-mined to hurt me? Just do as I ask, will you?" She walks away sobbing, saying, "Hell, that child is just like her father, cold as ice, and doesn't care about anyone but herself."

I want to smash her to pieces, to tell her she's so wrong about me. I care about everyone. It's me that keeps the family together. How dare she say such awful things? But I can't say anything, because she'd just disintegrate before my eyes and then blame me for it. So I grit my teeth, yet again, and make up the spare bed in my room for the grandma I've never met.

I look around my room. It's the only safe place I have in this house, where I can go when Dad's criti-cism of me and Mom's hysteria wear me out. But now I won't have anywhere to go, as there'll be a stranger invading the only space I have. My stomach churns, and it feels as if there's a monster festering and growing inside my intestines with nowhere to go.

When the bed's made, I go back downstairs.

"Did you put fresh towels on Grandma's bed?" Mom demands.

"No."

"Well, go and do it," she snaps. "Why d'you have to be told everything? You're making me ill, Marsha, don't you realize?"

I stomp upstairs again, the monster inside me growing by the second. Why can't she do it? Why do I have to do everything? I put three towels and a washcloth on Grandma's bed and go back downstairs to vacuum the living room.

"Be *careful*," she shouts, as I suck up something that rattles. "You'll break it."

I switch it off and shake the vacuum. A piece of glass drops to the floor. Mom must have broken a glass at some time and didn't pick up all the pieces. She's nagging me about breaking the vacuum, yet she doesn't care about whether the kids would have stepped on it and cut their feet. I walk out of the room and drop the shard in the trash, my jaw clenched as I struggle to control myself.

She pours herself a glass of whisky and takes a gulp with shaking hands. I start the vacuum again and push it this way and that, as Mom sits on the couch, drinking.

She rubs the side of her head and yells over the sound of the vacuum, "Can't you hurry? My head's killing me."

It might not hurt so bad if you'd just stop drinking, I think, but I don't say anything.

Eventually I've finished and it looks so much better. If I didn't feel so battered by Mom's tongue, I'd have felt pleased with myself.

Mom is like a cat on a hot tin roof as she paces the floor, glancing at the clock, and looking out of the window.

"What time is she coming?"

"Any time now," Mom slurs. "Start making dinner."

"What d'you want me to make?"

"Oh, I don't know. What is there?"

Mom has no idea what's going on in our house, and the fact that she doesn't know what's in the fridge proves it. I search for something to cook, but there's only snacky stuff, not anything with which to make a proper dinner. I tell her and she gets all flustered.

"Why didn't you tell me we needed more stuff?" she cries. She shakes her head, as if she can't believe how stupid I am, and goes to her purse.

"Here, go to the store and buy some pork chops and stuff to make a salad," she says, handing me twenty dollars. "And hurry up. Grandma could be here any minute, and we won't have anything to give her to eat. Honestly, Marsha, can't you see that I'm not well? You've got to do better."

I snatch the bill out of her hand and slam the door behind me. The monster inside me festers and grows, churning inside my intestines. I put my head down as I pass other kids who go to my school. It doesn't seem fair that they're able to hang out and have fun, while I'm stuck inside trying to make everything right for a mom I can't please.

They're still there when I walk back to the house with two full grocery bags. I bought some chocolate milk for the kids; I know they love it. But now I wish I hadn't, because the bags are heavy.

As I open the door, I can tell that Grandma has arrived because Mom's giggling like Shelley does when someone tickles her. She sounds like a silly kid. I walk into the living room, and standing there is a woman who looks like an older version of Mom. She's got too much makeup on, which is smudged, as she's obviously been crying, and she's got long hair that's been dyed blond. There's a dark line in the middle of her head where her roots are showing.

"Ah!" she wails, holding out her arms as she comes towards me. "You must be Marsha."

I stand there stiffly, with the bags by my side making my shoulders ache, as she throws her arms around me. I feel like choking as she's wearing too much perfume. She engulfs me and I pull my head back, trying to catch my breath.

"Hello," is all I can think of to say.

When she lets go of me, I go into the kitchen and dump the bags on the counter. I can hear Mom saying bad things about me.

"I'm sorry there's no dinner made. I have to get after Marsha all the time. You'd think she'd help more, what with Dad being away."

She bursts into tears and Grandma puts her arms around her, while I seethe in the kitchen. I slam the pork chops onto the grill, as the monster inside me writhes, begging to be released. Then I slam the lettuce on the chopping board and reach for a knife.

Grandma comes up behind me and says, "Marsha, you really should help your mother more. Can't you see that she's having a hard time? I'd help her myself if I weren't having a hard time, too." My head starts spinning with the injustice of it all, as this woman, who I've never met before, tells me I should do more, without knowing that I do *everything*. In an instant I hate her, and my guts churn even harder as she, too, bursts into tears.

"My husband, your grandfather, has just left me after all these years," she sobs.

She falls to pieces in front of me, as Mom's in the living room already in pieces, and I want to scream. But as always, I say nothing. I chop the lettuce and dump it into a bowl.

"When you're older, you'll understand and perhaps you'll show a little more compassion," Grandma says. "You need to support your mother, not make her life harder."

I grab a tomato, and it almost squashes in my hand as the monster inside me screams to be released. I take the knife and cut the tomato into slices with such a force that the knife slices across my finger. Bright red blood oozes out of me and onto the tomato.

Grandma shrieks, "Oh, no. Lillian, she's cut her finger, and there's blood all over the food."

"Oh, *now* what," I hear Mom say.

But that's the last thing I hear either of them say, even though I'm vaguely aware that they're fussing around me, for something weird happens to me. My body is bathed in a warm feeling as my finger smarts. I can actually *feel* something, pain, yet it doesn't really hurt. It's strange. But something even more amazing happens. The monster inside me, that has festered and grown and was about to burst out of me, coils back down, sleeping peacefully in my intestines.

Chapter Two

Mom and Grandma make such a fuss. They don't care about me; all they care about is the blood dripping on the tomatoes.

"Look what you've done," Mom cries. "That's disgusting."

She scoops the bloody tomato into the trash-can.

"D'you see what I mean?" she says to Grandma. "I swear she deliberately tries to upset me."

Grandma shakes her head. "Marsha, you *have* to make more of an effort to help your mom. You're almost grown."

"Get out of the way," Mom snaps, pushing me.

I wrap a piece of paper towel around my bleed-ing finger.

"Go on, get out. You did that deliberately to get out of cooking dinner," Mom shouts.

I turn around and leave the house. I walk towards

the kids' playground at the end of the street and sit on one of the swings. I remove the paper towel to look at my finger. The cut's pretty deep and it's oozing. It doesn't hurt, though. The blood fascinates me and again I feel a strange sense of calm come over me, as I watch the red beads glisten and grow. When they become too full and the beads pop, the blood runs down my finger.

Time seems to slip by, and it's only when the sun disappears that I think about going home. I let myself in, and immediately the kids run to me.

"Where have you been?" Mom demands.

I dare to answer back.

"You told me to get out, so I did."

"Don't sass me," Mom snaps. She sounds really edgy. I look around for her glass of whisky but I can't see one. Perhaps she doesn't want her mom to know she drinks.

I hunt through the kitchen drawers to find a band-aid and the kids hover around me, wanting to see.

"Does it hurt?" they ask, and I tell them "no."

Mom tells me to bathe the kids.

"But my finger's still bleeding," I protest.

"That's not *my* fault, is it?" she bites back at me.

I can see that there's no point to arguing, so I take the kids upstairs and try as best I can to bathe them with one hand. When they're in bed, I go to my room. I haven't eaten anything, and I can't be bothered. I'd rather go hungry than go downstairs and be with Mom and Grandma.

I lie on my bed and squeeze the cut to make it bleed, and the smarting gives me a strange sense of comfort. I mop up the blood in a tissue so that it doesn't mess up my sheets.

I'm just about to fall asleep when the door opens and Grandma snaps on the light. I groan and am fully awake again. She bustles around the room. I toss and turn, trying to get comfortable, but I give up and go to the bathroom. Why does she have to be in my room? Why can't the kids share, and she have one of their rooms? I decide to go downstairs and ask Mom.

She looks shocked when she sees me standing in the doorway, almost as if she's been caught doing something wrong. Then I get it; she waited until Grandma went to bed before pouring herself a drink. She doesn't want Grandma to know. I'm not surprised, the amount Mom drinks.

"What do *you* want?" she snaps at me.

I decide to try and appeal to her better nature, if she has one.

"Mom, why does Grandma have to share my room? Why can't the kids share and then she could have one of their rooms?"

Okay, so Mom doesn't have a better nature, especially when she's dying for a drink. She hisses at me, being careful not to make too much noise in case Grandma comes back downstairs and catches her with a large glass of whisky in her hand.

"Don't you start on me," she hisses. "I've got enough on my plate without you making it worse. Go to bed. You've made enough drama for one day."

I can see that there's no point in arguing with her as she turns her back on me and downs her drink in one gulp, before pouring another. I go back to my room and pull the pillow over my head to block out the light as Grandma reads. I'm so mad that I want to scream, but I hold it in and squeeze the cut on my finger, which seems to help, although I don't know why.

How come my mom is so unreasonable? Why won't she listen to me? Sometimes I think she hates me. She wouldn't even consider moving Grandma into the kids' room, which I'm sure Grandma would prefer. It's as if Mom enjoys making things difficult, or rather, enjoys making my life hell.

Grandma's still in bed when I get up and sort Casey and Shelley out, and I drop them off on my way to school. I have basketball practice tonight, and so I remind them that Mrs. Smythe will be taking them home.

"Oh, good," Casey says, "she always gets us some candy on the way home."

I wave goodbye as they hang up their coats and run off to find their little friends on the playground.

They look too small to be at school, and I feel a flash of guilt that I've been so moody lately; it's not their fault.

I catch up with Tessa, my friend, as I go through the school gates.

"What's wrong?" she asks.

I shrug. "The same stuff. Mom seems to have gone to pieces since Dad left for Iraq. Honestly, it's as if he's what keeps her in one piece, and now that he's gone, she's lost it. And to make things worse, her mother's come to stay. I know she's my grandma, but I don't know her. She seems just like Mom — hysterical. Her husband has left her...I don't know him either."

"What have you done to your finger?" Tessa asks.

"Oh, it's nothing. I caught it when I was making dinner last night." I don't tell her that I squeezed it in frustration and made it worse.

"You need a Band-Aid on that," is all she says.

I go to see the school nurse, and she stains it with something brown and then wraps a Band-Aid around it.

"Good as new," she says. "Be more careful next time."

I mutter, "It doesn't hurt," as I walk away.

I take my seat in class, and a lady called Miss Tina sits on the table in front of us. She comes to our school every week to talk to us about life and to help us with any problems we may have. Our teacher stays in the room, marking papers.

"Hi," she says. I like her but some of the kids try to give her a hard time. "Today we're going to talk about how it feels to have family members who are fighting the war over in Iraq."

She barely finishes speaking before a girl bursts into tears.

"My brother's over there," she cries. "I'm so scared for him."

"My dad's over there," another kid says.

"Mine, too," someone else calls out.

Our teacher looks up and he says, "My son joined the military a year ago. He's only nineteen, and he's over there, too."

Miss Tina looks at him and asks, "How are you coping?"

He puts his pen down and looks serious.

"It's strange, because part of me feels such pride that he's fighting the war on terrorism, but if I'm honest, the bigger part of me is absolutely terrified that I'll lose him."

I look at him as if I don't know him at all, and I guess I don't. He's always just *there*, telling us what to do, and to do it quietly.

"He was so eager to join up, and although I didn't try to stop him, I had hoped that boot camp would put him off; but it didn't. He loved it and seemed to enjoy a challenge. He got a real kick out of pushing himself. It was hard to watch him go. I had to pretend that I was okay, but I wasn't. And if he felt any fear, he didn't show it."

"So how are you coping?" Miss Tina asks him again. I guess he didn't answer her question.

He's quiet for a moment and then says, "Not very well, actually. I feel glued to the news; I don't want to hear it, but I can't help myself. It's almost as if I feel closer to him if I keep up to date on the latest out there, but everything I hear makes me sick with fear. I'm not sure how I'm coping. Um, I keep busy, and email him everyday. I try to focus upon being thankful that we can communicate through email; can you imagine what it would have been like before telephones and email?" He gives an involuntary shudder.

A boy in the back row says that he emails his dad everyday, too. He also says that his mom sits in front of the television all day, trying to keep up with the news.

"Trouble is, it makes her cry, and I don't know how to help her," he says.

I speak out. "My dad has always wanted to join the military, so when he got called up, he was ecstatic. It was like he didn't care about leaving us. Mom sits in front of the news, too, and spends most of the time crying." I don't tell them that she's drunk half the time, or that she's gone to pieces without Dad being around.

Miss Tina says, "We live in an age where, due to modern technology, we're lucky to be able to stay in contact with those who are fighting overseas, but the downside to it is that the same technology allows the war to enter our living rooms. It's compelling to watch the news, but being faced with it all the time increases our anxiety and fear for our loved ones."

Some of the kids agree; our teacher does, too.

"How can you cope with your fear?" she asks looking around the class.

No one says anything. She looks at the teacher.

"Like I said, I keep as busy as I can. I send him emails about everyday things so that he can feel close to home. It must be worse for him being stuck in an environment that's so different from home. Then I try to stay focused upon the fact that he's highly trained and not the little boy I remember who fell off his bike and cried when he skinned his knee."

He smiles.

"That must be hard," Miss Tina says.

"It is at times, but it's the one thing that really helps, because all the time that I remember him as a little boy, I get scared for him. But when I remind myself that he's a man and knows things about warfare that will keep him safe, that helps me to control my anxiety."

"Can any of you think that way?" Miss Tina asks the class.

The boy in the back row says, "My dad's a crack shot, and he's been in the military for years. I trust that he can keep himself and his men safe, but what about suicide bombers who don't care whether they die? That's what scares me. I just get scared that he'll be in the wrong place at the wrong time."

I don't think the same about my dad, because he hasn't had years of training. I hope he's had enough, but I can't be sure. What happens if *he's* in the wrong place at the wrong time? I shake the question from my head, feeling numb.

"Sometimes it helps to remind yourself of the odds against your loved ones being in the wrong place at the wrong time," Miss Tina says. "Thinking in that way can help you focus on positive thoughts rather than on negative ones. Dwelling on your fears will bring you down and lessen your ability to cope with the separation."

I barely hear anything else Miss Tina says. I don't want to think about it, and I'm glad when the class ends. I hurry out of the room with Tessa and go to my next class.

The day seems to take forever to go by, but finally it's time for basketball practice. I'm not very good at it and, although I go every week, I usually end up sitting out because the coach chooses someone else who's better than me. I only get to play once, and then I miss the shot and the team groans at me.

I walk home with Tessa and she tells me not to

take it so hard. It's okay for her; she's good at it. I say goodbye as we get to her house and I walk on towards mine.

I let myself in and hang up my jacket. Mom and Grandma are sitting on the sofa watching television. Mom looks up at me.

"Where are the kids?" she demands.

"What d'you mean? Mrs. Smythe drops them off when I have basketball practice, remember?"

"You never told me you had basketball today. We went out. I thought you were picking the kids up."

"I always have basketball on a Thursday."

Mom stands up. She's red in the face and steps towards me. "What's wrong with you, Marsha? Can't you see how upset I am? Don't you realize that I can barely keep up with what day it is? You need to remind me when you're going to be late."

Oh, so it's my fault, is it? How come I get blamed for everything? I don't know what comes over me; perhaps it's the injustice of it all, but I snap back at her.

"Perhaps if you weren't so drunk all the time, you'd know what day it is."

I don't see it coming but I feel it. She slaps me hard and screams at me, telling me how cold and heartless I am. She dissolves into tears. Grandma puts her arms around her and pats her shoulders.

"Marsha," Grandma says as if she hates me,

"how can you speak to your mother like that? You can see that she's having a hard time. You really are an ungrateful child."

My neck gets hot and I know my face is red. How dare this woman come into our home and start picking on me when it's *me* that does everything around here? I watch them comfort each other, and it dawns on me that they're so busy picking on me that neither has asked where the kids might be. They make me sick. I pick up the phone and call Mrs. Smythe.

"Did you drop the kids off today?" I ask.

"Yes, dear. I waited until I saw them open the gate. Why, is there something wrong?"

"Yes, Mom wasn't in. She'd gone out," I say, placing the blame back on her.

I can barely hear Mrs. Smythe as Mom screams at me, telling me that it was my fault. When I put the phone down, my stomach churns with anxiety. Where are my little brother and sister?

"You better get out there and find them," Grandma says. "For heaven sake, Marsha, can't you see your mother's upset? Do something!"

I grit my teeth and turn around without saying anything to her, but I feel hatred coursing through me. How dare she say such things and order me about? I slam the door hard after me to let her know that I hate her.

I run up the road, looking in our neighbors' gardens, but the kids aren't there. I cross over to the playground, but they aren't there either. I go the opposite direction and run until I have a stitch in my side. They are nowhere, so I go home.

"I can't find them," I say.

Mom is sitting on the sofa sobbing, and she doesn't seem to care that her mother can see her; she's got a large glass of whisky. Grandma's got one, too.

I feel sick with fear. "Have you called the police?" I ask.

Mom wails, and Grandma says, "No, we thought they'd be playing outside."

I feel contempt for both of them as I pick up the phone and dial 911. The words seem to come from someone else as I give the police the details. They say they'll send someone around.

As I put the phone down, I hear the man on the news say about a child who had been missing for two days. Mom howls, "That's in our neighborhood."

She stands up shakily, and steps towards me, her face distorted with hatred, as she starts flailing her arms, slapping at any part of me she can reach. She sounds like a crazy woman.

"If my babies have been taken by some pervert, I'll kill you myself. This is your fault."

I try to back away but she lunges at me, screaming and slapping.

I'm crying, partly out of shock, but also because I'm scared silly for my little brother and sister. I feel so guilty. If only I hadn't stayed behind for basketball, they'd be home safe. I'm no good at basketball anyway.

Grandma gets up and tries to pull Mom off me. I take a step back, and she helps Mom back to the sofa where they hold each other and say bad things about me.

I go into the kitchen, my heart hammering in my chest. My head is spinning so badly that I think I may faint. I can't believe the injustice of Mom and Grandma's words, but mostly I'm terrified. My hands are trembling and I don't know what makes me reach for a knife; it's as if I'm a puppet and someone is pulling my strings.

I take the knife and draw it over the inside of my forearm. In an instant a line of crimson bursts onto my skin, and all the pent-up tension that threatened to explode inside me is gone. I feel a warm glow spread through me as I watch the red beads slide down my arm. I draw the knife across my skin half an inch further up my arm and drop the knife into the sink, as I pull off a piece of kitchen towel. I dab the blood and watch it spring back in two parallel red lines across my arm. It distracts me from the anger and pain inside me.

I seem to have lost all sense of time, and as Mom's voice gradually filters back into the kitchen, I feel a sense of urgency. I can't be caught bleeding in the kitchen. I run upstairs with the paper towel pressed against my wounds.

"Where are you going?" Mom demands. "Come back down here."

Grandma stands at the bottom of the stairs and calls up to me. She's slurring.

"Marsha, *please* come down and help your mother."

I stay in my room, watching the blood from the cuts on my arm slow to a glistening railway track. My head tells me that it should hurt, but it doesn't. I can hear Mom and Grandma downstairs and it seems as if the whole world has gone mad, and I can't do one single thing to control it. But I *can* control the tension inside me; I've found a way. I smile to myself and feel calmer than I have since Dad left for Iraq.

There's a knock on the door, and I hear a man talking. I change my top for one with long sleeves and go downstairs.

A policeman is standing in our living room and Mom's crying all over again.

"We're doing everything we can, Ma'am. I'm sure they'll turn up. Do they have any friends they like to play with, or a special place they like to go?"

Mom can't answer; she doesn't know. She makes me sick. She doesn't even know what Casey and Shelley like to do.

I tell the policeman that they never play with

other children in the neighborhood, as Dad won't allow them to play outside the yard.

"They like candy," I say. "Mrs. Smythe, that's the lady who brings them home when I have basketball practice, usually takes them to buy some candy."

I give him Mrs. Smythe's phone number and he leaves, saying that he'll be in touch.

Grandma tells me to make some dinner for Mom, who needs her strength. How can they eat? I can't. I have a huge knot in my stomach. I don't think I'll ever be able to eat again.

I don't say anything, though, and go into the kitchen to grill some chicken. I move as if I'm in a dream, but I'm okay because I've got a secret weapon. If they make me mad and I can't cope, I know what to do to make myself feel better. The slight stinging from my arm distracts me as I watch the peas boil and the fries bubble in the fryer.

Mom and Grandma don't even say "Thank you" when I put a plate in front of them. Grandma pours more whisky for Mom and herself. "Go on," she says to Mom, "get that inside you. You'll feel better."

Now I understand why Grandpa used to be so mean about Mom and her mother. Grandma doesn't help my mom; she encourages her to be "useless," that's what Grandpa called her.

I sit and watch the news, and images of American soldiers lying dead on the ground flash across the screen. I think about the things Miss Tina said in class today about being glued to the news but it adding to the anxiety. I feel tears prick my eyes. If I'm really honest, I don't care that my dad isn't at home every night because he could be mean, but I don't want him in Iraq where he might end up lying dead in a ditch because he was in the wrong place at the wrong time. I'm angry with myself because I can't stop the tears from falling down my face. Even though life with Dad at home wasn't always easy, it was better than this. Mom seems to have totally lost it since he left, and having Grandma here has made her worse. I wish Dad were here. I'd even march up and down the path with a broomstick over my shoulder as a pretend gun, if he could just come home and take control of Mom again.

The man on the television reports that another helicopter was shot down and ten American soldiers were killed. I feel sick and I go to turn it off, but Mom shouts at me, "Leave that on. Don't be so selfish; you know I need to hear what's going on in Iraq."

My teeth clench with hatred, and this time I walk purposefully to the kitchen and retrieve the knife from the sink. I slice two more lines on my arm. I exhale a deep breath as I watch the blood ooze out, and I feel the tension that's been boiling inside me ebb away.

By the time Mom and Grandma have finished eating, the blood has stopped flowing and I can pull my sleeve over the cuts, confident that no blood will seep through and give my secret away.

Grandma brings the plates out into the kitchen, but she ignores me and is obviously mad at me. I rinse them off and put them in the dishwasher. The doorbell rings.

"Get that, will you?" Mom calls from the living room.

I open the door, and standing in front of me is a policeman. I gasp, as beside him is Shelley.

I grab her and hug her so close to me that she squirms, trying to get away. She brushes against my sliced arm and I welcome the pain, but then it dawns on me.

"Where's Casey?" I ask.

Mom and Grandma are behind me, and Mom sobs all over again.

"Where's Casey?" I ask again, with fear lodged in my stomach. I'm glad I haven't eaten because I'm about to throw up.

"Can I come in?" the policeman asks, stepping into the house without waiting for an answer.

We go into the living room and sit down. Shelley ignores Mom and Grandma and comes to sit on my knee. I hold her close to me and stroke her hair. I love her so much.

"We found her wandering about downtown. She said that when no one was home..."

He doesn't get to finish his sentence before Mom

says, "That was Marsha's fault."

I feel such hatred towards her, but I can't show it because I don't want Shelley to get upset.

The policeman ignores her, and carries on. "When they found no one home, it seems that they walked back to the candy store. Shelley told us that a man bought them candy and then said he'd take them home."

"My legs were aching," Shelley says innocently. "I didn't want to walk anymore."

Mom begins to howl, and my stomach is so sick that I need the bathroom. Tears flow down my face and I'm filled with dread. It's like listening to the news reporter... you want to listen, yet you don't. Mom's howling so loudly that we can't hear what Shelley's saying.

The policeman sounds kind, but firm, and says, "Ma'am, please listen to your little girl."

Mom sniffs and then falls silent.

"I didn't want to walk anymore. I wanted a ride home so I said 'Yes' but Casey said 'No.' The man gave me more candy, but Casey pulled my arm and he hurt me. I don't like Casey anymore." She starts crying, and I stroke her hair, trying to calm her down.

"What happened?" I ask.

"Casey ran away, and wouldn't wait for me. I tried to catch up with him but I couldn't."

"And what happened to the man?" I ask.

She looks confused and shrugs. "I dunno."

"Where's Casey?"

"I dunno."

The policeman speaks to Mom. "Ma'am, we have a situation here. Shelley was found wandering around downtown. Casey apparently ran off, and we're hoping that he's wandering around somewhere, lost. But there's always a chance that the man followed him. I'm sorry. We've got everyone out looking for him. Try and have faith."

"Faith?" she cries. "How can I have faith? Marsha, this is all your fault." She starts sobbing all over again, and as she blames me, a tiny thought creeps into my head. Even though Shelley could have been taken by the man, Mom's ignored her. She hasn't hugged her or tried to make her feel better. It occurs to me that the way my mom thinks, everything is about her.

Chapter Three

The policeman leaves and says that he'll be in touch as soon as he has any news. He says it just like that, as if he'll let us know the results of a baseball game when he knows them. I want to scream. I'm trembling and I feel sick.

Shelly clings to my neck and looks scared as Mom and Grandma cry. I try to reassure her, but my heart's not in it. What can I say? She's too little to understand our fear.

Mom almost spits at me; there's hatred in her voice. "If anything has happened to my little boy, I'll never forgive you."

Oh, so now he's "her little boy." It's a shame she doesn't feel that way all the time. She can't be bothered with him or Shelley. If she hates me, that's nothing to the hatred I feel towards her right this minute, as Shelley's arms cling to my neck. I can't say the things I want to say, so I carry Shelley upstairs to get her ready for bed.

I tuck her in but Mom doesn't even bother to come upstairs to kiss her goodnight. I shake my head in disbelief; what kind of mother is she? A drunk, that's what.

I go back downstairs, and she and Grandma are drinking whisky again. Mom's face is flushed. She looks at me and starts.

"Are you *trying* to drive me crazy, Marsha? How could you do this to me? You know how hard it is for me without Dad here."

Grandma joins in, and I think I hate her more than I do my mother. She doesn't even know me. She doesn't know how I've held this family together, yet she launches into me, with blame dripping off her.

"It's not my fault," I try to say above the hateful things they're saying. "I always play basketball on a Thursday. You know that. You should have been home when the kids were dropped off."

"Don't you dare blame me," Mom screams at me, suddenly hysterical. "It's not my fault you didn't remind me that you were playing basketball."

I can't help the sarcasm that flows from me. "Well, if you weren't so hung over every morning, perhaps you'd know what was going on with your kids."

Mom lunges at me, her hands slapping at my face.

"Don't you dare speak to your mother like that," Grandma says. "Show some respect."

I step back so that Mom can't hit me anymore, and she staggers to the sofa and collapses, sobbing loudly. Grandma looks as if she despises me, as she goes over to Mom and holds her.

"Marsha," Shelley calls from the top of the stairs. "I'm scared."

I look at Mom and Grandma, who are oblivious to Shelley, and I feel contempt for them. I go up the stairs and take Shelley back to bed, but she's crying and won't stop.

I take her to my room and cuddle her on my bed, hoping that she'll fall asleep. She fights it, though, and every time she drifts off, she seems to wake with a jolt. She nestles into me and brushes against the cuts on my arm. A pain shoots through me and, although I wince, I'm glad the pain is there; it seems easier to bear than the pain that lives inside me.

Eventually Shelley falls asleep, and I gently carry her back to her bed. I go to my room, not wanting to go downstairs to be around Mom and Grandma, especially as they're drinking. I sit on my bed at the window with the light off and stare at the dark shapes of the trees outside. I wonder where Casey is. Is he afraid in the dark? As I think it, a tear rolls down my cheek. I can't bear to think of him being out there in the dark all alone. But then I pray that he *is* alone, and not with the man who wanted to give the kids a ride home. I'm so freaked out by my thoughts that I cry and cry; they're silent tears, though, so that no one can hear me.

Mom's words echo in my head, "It's not my fault you didn't remind me that you were playing basketball." I didn't remind her. Okay, she *was* hung over and asleep when I left to take the kids to school, but I could have left her a note to remind her. My stomach churns as I blame myself. I know Mom's lost it since Dad left. I know she's not coping. I should have left her a note. A small voice inside tells me that even if I had left a note, I couldn't be sure that Mom would have acted on it. The same voice argues with me and says that I shouldn't have stayed behind at school to play basketball... I'm rubbish at it anyway. I should have been home making sure that the kids were okay.

The pain in my stomach is so bad that I clamp my hand over my mouth, as a howl threatens to escape from me. I rock to and fro as I stare outside at the darkness. I want to cut myself. I can't bear the pain inside me. I can't stand it. I have to cut; I just have to.

Suddenly I feel as if something furtive has crept over me, and I stop rocking. I am driven by a purpose. I creep downstairs, determined that I won't allow Mom and Grandma to see me. There's no chance that they'll notice me as they're sitting on the sofa, deep in conversation, saying hateful things about me. I open the drawer gently and retrieve a small kitchen knife. I hover in the doorway until I'm sure they're looking the other way, and then I dart up the stairs as quietly as I can. My room is a temporary haven.

I leave the light off, so that no one can see into our house from the outside; so that no one can see into my soul. I sit on my bed by the window, and as I stare at the dark shapes outside and imagine my little brother being terrified in the dark, all alone, I take the knife in my left hand and slice my right arm. Even in the dark I can see the shadow of my blood, a line across my forearm. The stinging distracts me from the agony inside me, as I blame myself for Casey being lost in the dark.

I hear a siren in the distance, and I'm filled with dread that at any moment a policeman will knock on our door and tell us that Casey's dead. I can barely breathe, and I start to rock again as silent sobs rasp my throat. I want to die; I want it all to go away. I want my Dad to come home and chase the madness away. My heart's pounding in my chest and I feel as if I'm going to explode.

I take the knife and draw it over my right forearm again, and as I think of Casey being dead, I draw it across my skin again and again. It's like magic; the blood and the stinging take me away from this room, where the blame and the pain in my heart threaten to engulf me.

I feel numb, but calm, like a puppet, as I blot the lines on my forearm so that they don't drip all over my bed. They seem to stop bleeding very quickly, and I'm left with angry, red, open gashes that speak of the rage inside of me as my voice is silenced.

I lie on my bed, my curtains open, so that I can see the darkness. My clock ticks loudly, slowly. I can't sleep.

I hear Grandma come upstairs and she opens my door. As a shaft of light exposes me lying rigidly on my bed, she stumbles into my room and I hear Shelley cry out.

I ignore Grandma and get to my feet, pulling my sleeves down over my knuckles so that she can't see my arms. I walk past her hoping that she'll feel my hatred for her.

Shelley's crying and begs to be allowed to sleep with me. I take her into my room and hold her tight. She cries, calling for Casey. I turn away so that she can't see my tears. It's hard to be strong for her, and it's even harder knowing that there's no one who's strong for me.

Grandma sits on the edge of her bed and seems to wobble while she plans what to say.

"Stop that noise," she blurts out. "You'll upset your mother."

I'm so angry with her that I blurt out, too, only I set out to manipulate her.

"Grandma, go and sleep in Shelley's room, then

you'll get some peace, okay?"

She attempts to stand up and staggers towards the door and heads towards Shelley's room. A bleak smile slides onto my face. At last, she's gone.

I try to put Shelley in Grandma's bed but she's not having any of it. She clings to my neck and murmurs, "No."

I give up in the end and curl myself around her, but sleep evades me. My stomach churns over and over thinking about Casey and wondering where he is. I long to get up and go outside to look for him, but every time I move, Shelley grabs me. I can't leave her. Silent tears roll down my face. I don't know how to deal with any of this. I wish I were dead, but even as I wish it, I know that I could never leave my little brother and sister.

I lie in my bed as stiff as a board, desperate not to wake Shelley once she finally falls asleep, yet my mind's racing and I'm plunged more and more into despair. Where is Casey? I can't sleep without knowing where he is. And as I think such thoughts, I'm aware that I've acknowledged the possibility that he may be dead. I want to know where he is, dead or alive. I hate the direction my thoughts are heading, but I don't seem to have any control over them.

I feel as if I'm drowning in despair and there's no one to rescue me, and right this minute, I don't feel that I'm worth rescuing. If I hadn't stayed behind to play basketball, Casey would be asleep in his bed right now. Silent tears flow down my face as I lie stock-still, afraid to wake Shelley up.

I drift in and out of consciousness as sleep battles to take me down, and at first I can't be sure if I'm dreaming or not when I hear ringing in my ears.

I extract myself from Shelley gently and she stirs. It's pitch black outside. I glance at my clock. It's four o'clock in the morning. I must be dreaming, but no, someone's ringing our doorbell.

Neither Mom nor Grandma wake up. I guess they're in a drunken stupor. I pad down the stairs in my furry slippers and head towards the front door.

"Who is it?" I ask, feeling silly.

"The police."

My stomach lurches; I'm about to learn the awful truth...Casey's dead.

"Can you open the door?" a man asks.

I fumble; my fingers don't seem to work. I open the door and my senses are assaulted. My head spins and my heart races. The pain inside me floats away to a place that's temporarily out of reach. There in front of me is a policeman holding Casey.

He doesn't wait to be invited into the house, and I shut the door behind him.

"Where's your mother?" he asks.

"In bed, drunk," I add. "Casey..."

I feel a sob escape me, as he puts my little brother in my arms. My sleeves ride up, and for a moment the policeman stares at me, reading every-thing that's inside me. I yank my sleeves back down and focus upon Casey, hoping that he'll ignore what he's just seen.

"Mom," I shout. "Get up."

I'm embarrassed because Mom's so drunk that she doesn't wake up immediately. I hand Casey back to the policeman and go upstairs to Mom's room. I shake her hard.

"What, what? Gerrof me."

"Mom, the police are here. They found Casey and he's okay. *Get up!*"

Mom staggers out of bed and goes down the stairs carefully. She looks at Casey and starts cry-ing. She grabs him off the policeman and sits on the sofa rocking. Casey struggles to get free from her. He comes to me and I pick him up; my heart soars with relief. I love my little brother so much.

"What happened?" I ask the policeman. "Where's he been?"

"He was found three miles away, wandering about in a neighborhood. He said that after run-ning away from the man who bought him candy, he thought he recognized his own neighborhood and walked the streets trying to find his house.

I hold him tight, and my life changes in an instant. I vow to do better. God has given me my brother and sister back, and I'm going to do anything and everything to make sure that they're safe and okay.

I don't care what it costs me.

Mom stands and sways, as the policeman is about to leave. As he goes, he looks at me with something in his eyes that I can't fathom. I take Casey upstairs and put him in his room.

Within minutes he wanders along the hall and opens my door.

"I want to sleep with you, Marsha."

I give up. I'm so grateful that he's safe that I'll agree to anything.

"Come on," I say pulling back the covers, the tension in my stomach ebbing away. "No snoring, though, okay?"

He runs across my room and climbs over Shelley, who amazingly is sound asleep, and he wedges himself between us.

I feel his body relax as he starts to breathe deeply and sleep steals over him. My head spins with silent prayers of thanksgiving. Right now I feel that I'd give *anything* to God for bringing Shelley and Casey home safely, and as I offer my silent prayers, I vow to give up basketball practice. The kids need me; I can't rely on Mom.

I feel half dead when the alarm goes off, and I turn it off before it wakes the kids. I'm not going to school today. I've had less than two hours sleep, the same as Casey. It's not enough, so I drift back to sleep.

Mom wakes me later as she opens my door and

demands to know why I haven't taken the kids to school.

"Mom, it was after four when the police brought Casey home. He'd be too tired to go to school."

I don't bother to tell her that I'd be too tired as well. Shelley's already gone downstairs; she's hungry, I guess. I yawn and stretch. Casey frowns.

"Ugh! Blood. Your arms have got hurts on them."

I yank my pajama sleeves down over my thumbs and tell him it's nothing. He looks at me as if I'm broken, or something. I distract him.

"C'mon, let's go and get you some breakfast. Are you hungry?"

He jumps out of bed and seems to forget about my arms instantly. I follow him downstairs. He seems completely unconcerned about the fright we had last night. I'm glad he's not affected by any of it, but I feel exhausted.

Mom barely speaks to me and I'm glad. I make some coffee for her and Grandma, too. She doesn't speak to me either. Mom switches the television on and turns over to watch the news. I make them some toast.

I hear Mom gasp and say, "Oh no, that's where Dad is. Oh, God, I can't stand the strain."

"What?" I ask.

"Shhh," Mom hisses at me.

I go into the living room to hear.

"Six soldiers were killed and ten injured when a suicide bomber blew himself up in Basra."

When the news anchor goes on to talk about a panda having given birth, Mom cries, "Oh, God, what if Dad's been hurt? What if he's been killed?" She begins to sob, and although I feel dread creep over me, I try to remember the things Miss Tina said in class.

"There must be thousands of soldiers in Basra, so the chances that it's Dad who's been hurt must be very small."

I should have kept my mouth shut because she turns on me and snaps, "How can you be so insensitive?" She shakes her head as if she can't believe how awful I am.

"I wasn't being insensitive," I dare to protest, "I was just trying to tell you what this lady at school said. She said that the chances of being in the wrong place at the wrong time were very slim, and that we can scare ourselves more if we choose to focus on negative things."

Mom seems to explode. "I do *not* focus on negative things. How dare you say that? What the hell does she know, anyway? I bet she doesn't have a husband out in Iraq. Are you telling me that I shouldn't be scared when I hear that six soldiers have been killed and ten injured in the same town your dad's in? You *are* insensitive. You're cold, just like your dad."

I walk away feeling battered. I was only trying to help her, but it seems that no matter what I say or do, it's wrong. I give up.

Grandma tells me to clear the table.

"Stop upsetting your mother. Honestly, Marsha, what's wrong with you? She's out of her mind with worry and you seem to enjoy upsetting her."

I feel such hatred for this woman who's only now bothered to come into my life, and who seems down on me for no reason. Something seems to die inside me... I was trying to help Mom, not upset her. I don't care if I offend Grandma, so I answer back.

"I was *not* trying to upset her, I was trying to help her."

"Don't you sass me, young lady," she bites back.

"I'm not sassing you," I say, "I'm just saying that I was trying to help her. Miss Tina held a class at school to help us cope with missing family members who're fighting in Iraq."

Grandma looks blank as I try to stick up for myself. It's as if she doesn't really hear me. Then it dawns on me; they're both suffering from a hangover and thinking probably hurts.

"Just clear the table," Grandma says, sweeping aside my reasoning.

I walk away to get a dishcloth. I feel anger festering inside me, and a thought pops into my head. I never liked Grandpa when he said mean things about Mom and her mother, but now I understand. Perhaps he wasn't being mean after all; he was just saying it how it was.

Mom turns up the television and starts pacing the floor. I can't stand it so I decide to take the kids out.

As I leave I say, "I'm taking the kids to the playground. I'll be back later in time to fix dinner." I hear myself being reasonable and I curse myself. Why should I bother when Mom and Grandma aren't reasonable towards me?

The kids are excited and ask where we're going. Their little faces shine with excitement and I wish that I could be that innocent. I take their hands and, although they're jumping about, I feel heavy and weighed down. Somewhere deep inside me are thoughts that compete with Miss Tina's reasoning, that tell me my dad could be hurt or dead. I'm scared but I try desperately to keep Miss Tina's words in my head.

The kids distract me as we get to the playground. They run and shout, telling me to watch them as they go headfirst down the slide. They dart from one thing to the next and their energy exhausts me, but I force myself to smile. The sight of them makes me want to cry. I'm the only one they've got. Mom and Grandma don't care. I *have* to take better care of them. It's hard, because the way I feel right now, I can hardly take care of myself. As I think it, I rip a small hole in the cuffs of my sleeves and poke my thumbs through, anchoring my sleeves down so that no one can see my wounds, my shame.

My arms sting; they don't really hurt, they just smart like a nagging sore that reminds me I'm alive. The discomfort is preferable to the awful pain inside me. It releases some of the stress that's about to blow up inside me. It gives me control over what happens to me when I have no control at home. My thoughts confuse me and I feel my stomach churn with anxiety. The urge to cut washes over me in a powerful wave, and as it engulfs me, I feel fear and powerlessness — I don't have my knife with me. I vow to carry it with me at all times, so that I'm in control of myself.

I feel so bad that I *have* to go home. I bribe the kids to leave the playground by telling them we'll stop off at the candy store on the way home. They charge after me, their faces shining.

Something vile creeps into my mind. Perhaps I'm just like my mom. She's addicted to alcohol to help her cope, and here I am, addicted to cutting myself so that *I* can cope. I feel sick as the possibility that I may be just like her dawns on me, but it doesn't stop the urge inside me.

The kids skip alongside me and I buy them each a bag full of candy. I warn them only to take candy from people they know, and never to take it from strangers. They glance at each other and then at me.

"What, like that man?"

"Yes, exactly like that man. Never take candy from strangers and never go with them, okay?"

"Okay," they both say together.

My thoughts momentarily float away, as I see anxiety flash across their little faces. I bob down so that my eyes are at their level.

"Are you okay?" I ask. "Did the man hurt you at all?"

"Yes."

"No."

They look confused and I understand. I realize that I've asked them two questions at one time. I start again.

"Are you okay?"

"Yes."

"Yes."

"Did the man hurt you?"

"No."

"No."

"Well, thank God. *Never* go with someone you don't know, and *never* take candy from strangers, okay?"

"Okay."

"Okay."

"C'mon, let's go home and make some dinner. Who wants to help?"

"Me."

"Me."

I struggle with my feelings as we walk home. Although the kids are dawdling, I try to hurry them up. I don't feel in control of myself without having access to a knife. I grip the kids' hands and playact at being cheerful. They don't notice the shadow that lurks behind my smile.

As we turn into our road my heart almost stops; the police are there again. Perhaps they've caught the evil man who tried to take Shelley and Casey away. The kids are too busy digging in their bags of candy to be hurried.

I feel as if I'm not really here, not really inside my body. I feel buried beneath thoughts that are tumbling in on me, but I can't pluck a single thought out from the mess that's in my head.

I grab the kids' hands and all but run down the road. As I open the door, I know something's wrong, and the police aren't here to tell us that they've caught the man. Mom would be happy if they had caught him, but she's howling. I feel dread creep up into my stomach, and I feel sick.

"Oh, there you are," Grandma snaps. "Where have you been? Your mother's been worried sick."

"I took the kids to the playground," I say. "I told you as I left."

They brush my words aside and I'm confused. It's like they aren't interested in where we've been. If they're not bothered about where we've been, then why are they so upset with me? Anxiety flows through me. Oh no. Please don't tell me that the police are here because of the TV announcement earlier. It can't be, it just can't be, but it is.

It's the same policeman who brought Casey back in the middle of the night. He looks at me, and I feel naked beneath his gaze, but not in a bad way; I feel that he can see into my soul. He seems to rescue me from my Grandma's caustic words.

"It's Marsha, isn't it?"

I nod.

"Come and sit down."

My stomach's sick. I can't cope with what I know he's going to tell me. I want to scream. It's like the whole world has gone mad. In less than twenty-four hours, I've lived with the fear that my little brother and sister had been killed, and now I have to face the fact that my father's dead. I'm too young for all of this.

"Your dad's been hurt."

"You mean, he's not dead?"

The policeman shakes his head and looks a bit confused.

"No. Why d'you think that?"

"Because Mom and Grandma automatically thought he was dead when they heard the news earlier."

"It's easy to become scared of fear. When people are frightened, they stop thinking clearly. I think your mom is scared for your father, and that's a normal feeling, Marsha. It's a jungle in Iraq at the moment; you'd be stupid not to be scared."

I feel ashamed of myself for being angry with my mom.

"Is my dad okay?"

He wears a sad face; one that I'm sure he's worn loads of times before, one that he learned in college... "How to give bad news successfully so that *you* don't feel bad."

"No, my love, he's not. He was one of the soldiers injured today. He's in a military hospital, but the army will be flying him home in four weeks."

"What's wrong with him?"

Mom howls loudly. The policeman shoots her a warning look and she stops immediately. Even though my head's spinning as I try to come to terms with what the policeman's telling me, I feel a sense of satisfaction that someone is strong enough to make my mom stop being so hysterical and dramatic. I ignore her and focus upon him.

"Honey, I hate to tell you this, but today when six of your dad's colleagues died, your dad was injured."

"How?" I whisper.

"He's in the hospital now. They had to operate on him to save his life..." He coughs uncomfortably. "...He lost both his legs."

Chapter Four

Something vile threatens to suffocate me, and I'm barely aware that I speak.

"No, you're lying. You have to be. No!"

The policeman pats my hand. "I'm so sorry, honey. There's nothing I can say to make it better."

A sick and bizarre thought pops into my head and I blurt out. "Well, Dad won't be able to make Casey march up and down the garden path anymore."

The policeman looks at me oddly.

It takes me a second to realize that the noise I hear is coming from Mom as she rears up from the sofa and lunges at me like a crazy woman. If I thought that having a policeman sitting in our living room would control Mom in some way, I was wrong — she grabs my hair and slaps me over and over.

The policeman jumps up and pulls her off me.

"Did you hear what she said? Did you? She's an insensitive little brat."

"That's right," Grandma chips in. "I mean, how could she say such a thing? She's cruel."

I'm crying, not only because my head hurts where Mom's wrenched at my hair and slapped me hard, but because I'm ashamed of myself. How could I have said something so insensitive? Perhaps I am unfeeling like my dad.

"I'm sorry, Mom," I cry, meaning it. "I don't know what made me say such a thing. I didn't mean to."

She doesn't listen to me and is crying harder than I am. Shelley and Casey stand in the doorway looking scared.

"Hello, Casey," the policeman says, but Casey doesn't answer him. Both kids run over to me, and I put my arms around them because they look frightened. I harden myself, trying to be strong. The wounds on my arms sting as the kids jostle for position on my lap.

It feels as if the whole world has gone crazy and is being acted out in our living room.

"Ma'am," the policeman says to Mom, raising his voice slightly to get her attention. "People say and do all kinds of things when they hear bad news. It's shock. Marsha spoke out and hurt your feelings, but you reacted badly towards her. Now, I'm not going to arrest you for hitting your child, although I should. You're in shock, and just this once I'm going to let it go, but only this once."

Mom looks at him as if he's not human.

"What?"

Grandma speaks out. "She was provoked. You heard what the child said. She tries to upset her mother all the time. It's constant. I've never known such a child. None of my children would have behaved so badly."

My head spins as I hear the things they're saying about me; it feels crazy. Mom and Grandma make out that I'm this horrible person and yet two little kids ignore *them* and run to *me* for comfort. I don't get it.

I don't think the policeman gets it either. He looks at me and the kids, and then at Mom and Grandma.

"I want you to listen to me," he says. "People react differently when they hear bad news. They're in shock. All of you are in shock." He looks as if he's struggling to find the right words to help us. "Don't take your fear and pain out on each other. Try and pull together. You'll need each other in the coming months."

He looks lost, and I get the feeling that he didn't learn those words at some college. Mom and Grandma fall silent, and suddenly I want him to move in. I don't want him to leave, because I feel a tiny little bit safer with him around. Okay, he didn't prevent Mom from pulling my hair or slapping me, but I could see the disbelief on his face, and it anchored me to a place where I know he thought, "This is crazy." His presence stops me from thinking that I'm going totally crazy while everything around me is falling apart.

"That's fine for you to say," Grandma says, "but you don't realize how destructive Marsha can be. It's like she's constantly trying to hurt her Mom," she pauses, and then adds, "well, and me. My husband's just left me after all these years, and you'd think that she'd be a bit more sympathetic, but no, all she does is cause trouble."

I feel as if they're talking about someone else, and I get the wildest urge to stick up for that person until I realize that they're talking about me. I shake my head, dodging the kids who are clambering on me. I glance desperately at the policeman, hoping that he'll help me. He glances at me.

"It sounds to me as if you're not really communicating with each other."

Mom and Grandma bristle.

"I'm finding it a bit hard to understand," he says. "You're describing someone who doesn't care about anyone, yet all I can see is a child, yes, a *child*, who is taking care of herself and two little children. If she were a mean person, the children wouldn't want to be with her. Believe me, children know who's mean and who isn't."

I love him instantly and decide that if I ever get married, I'm going to marry someone just like him.

Mom and Grandma sniff and look mad.

"From what I'm seeing, I think that you're all under a lot of stress since your husband, Ma'am, left for Iraq, and that's understandable. Try and find a way to talk to each other rather than hurt each other; that's all I'm saying."

He stands to leave and I feel a flash of panic. I don't want him to go.

"Marsha, will you walk out with me?" he asks, ruffling Casey's hair.

I feel Mom and Grandma's eyes bore into my back as I extract myself from the kids and follow him through the door. I tell the kids to go and play in the back yard, and they reluctantly go after I ask them four times.

I follow the policeman out of the house and we get to his car. He leans against it.

"Call me Evan, okay?"

I nod, feeling awkward.

"I may be old, but I'm not dumb," he says, and part of me dreads what he's going to say next. I know that he can see how crazy my life is inside my house, but if he can see that, he can see what's going on inside me, too. "You're in trouble, aren't you?"

"No," I say defensively.

"Marsha, I'm not stupid. I saw your arms last night. You're cutting, aren't you?"

I look away and wipe a betraying tear away with

my cuff that's anchored around my thumb so that my sleeve can't ride up and betray me. He touches my shoulder.

"Listen, I know it's hard for you at the moment. Your mom needs help, so does your grandma. I want you to talk to someone, okay? Her name is Miss Tina."

I turn around to face him, not caring if my eyes are glistening with tears.

"I know Miss Tina. She comes to our school. She tried to help us cope with having someone in our family fighting the war in Iraq. I tried to tell Mom the things she told us but she went crazy... there's no talking to her. Miss Tina said that focusing upon negative things increases our fear, but when I tried to tell Mom that, she went mad. There's nothing Miss Tina can say that'll help me."

I feel suffocated by my feelings of despair and hopelessness.

"I'm not talking about coping with family members in Iraq, I'm talking about hurting so much inside that you feel the need to cut yourself."

Although the sun is beating down on me, I shiver involuntarily. I knew he saw my arms last night. I'm so mad at myself. Why wasn't I more careful? He seems to see through me as if I'm transparent, and I have nowhere to hide. I don't know how to feel towards someone who forces me to face myself, so in an instant I hate him and change my mind about marrying someone like him.

He gets into the patrol car and hands me his card.

"Call me if you need to talk, okay? And talk to Miss Tina at school."

Mom cries throughout the whole evening, and I go to bed early to get away from her. The kids sleep in my room again, but at least I manage to get them to lie in Grandma's bed rather than mine. I lie there waiting for sleep to come over me, but I just toss and turn.

I don't know how I get through the next four weeks. Mom cries all the time, and I feel sick with apprehension thinking about how it's going to be when Dad gets home. Mom's on the phone all the time, trying to get information about Dad and how he's doing. Grandma seems to be in a panic, and I wonder whether it's because Dad doesn't know she's staying with us... I know he doesn't like her.

I hope she'll go home, but as the weeks pass, she stays. She says Mom's going to need all the help she can get. I think it's going to be Dad that needs all the help he can get, not Mom. I watch the kids like a hawk and try to prepare them for when Dad comes home. I see Tessa at school but don't hang out with her anymore, as I'm too scared to leave the kids alone with Mom and Grandma. She calls me sometimes, but Mom tells me to get off the phone in case there's a call from Dad.

I see Miss Tina at school each week and I avoid her. She looks at me in class and calls on me to answer her questions. I get paranoid, thinking that Evan has told her about me cutting myself, so I avoid her. She calls me as the bell signals the end of the class.

"Marsha, come here."

Tessa goes on with the others and I stare at the floor, twitching my thumbs to make sure my sleeves are anchored down.

"Are you all right?" she asks.

"Yes."

"I hear your dad is coming home soon. I know that has to be hard. If you ever need anyone to talk to, please call me. Will you do that?"

I just want her to go away, so I promise anything to shut her up. I don't want to talk to her or anyone else. She hands me a card.

"This is where I work, Beach Haven. The phone number's on there, and there's an email address too. If you ever need anyone to talk to, please reach out, Marsha, don't suffer alone."

My face burns and I want to get away from her. I like her, but the things she says strip me of my resolve to stay strong, and I can't handle it.

I slip the card into my bag and catch up with Tessa.

"What did she want?"

"Oh, nothing."

I pick up the kids on the way home, as I do every day. We turn the corner into our road and instantly I freeze. There's a police car outside our house. I'm filled with dread. I hurry the kids along the road and let myself into the house.

Mom's crying. Evan's there and I'm glad to see him, although being around him makes me nervous. Grandma's flustered and is trying to take charge.

"Lillian, sit down. Let's move this chair out of the way and then you'll have more room."

Dad turns around when he hears the door open. I feel tears prick my eyes. My dad is sitting in a wheelchair; his body stops at the edge of the seat. Empty pant legs are folded beneath two fat stumps. I feel sick and I don't know what to do.

I go over to him and place a kiss on his cheek.

"Welcome home, Dad," I say, knowing that it's inadequate, but I don't know what to say.

His jaw quivers but there are no tears in his eyes. He looks angry.

"I hear you've been giving Mom and Grandma a hard time since I left. Marsha, I was counting on you to help. What's gotten into you?"

I don't know how to answer. I feel so betrayed that I say nothing.

"See?" Mom cries and dissolves into tears again.

The kids stand in front of Dad with their mouths open. They seem unable to go near him. We stare awkwardly at each other, and God forgive me, but

I feel revolted. I feel so bad; I must be the worst person in the world. Seeing Dad with no legs freaks me out. I want to hug him and tell him that I'm glad he's alive and back home, but he's just attacked me without knowing what's been going on in our house since he left. I feel really angry with him, and then I feel guilty for feeling angry with someone who's disabled.

I say nothing and am overwhelmed by the need to cut myself. Over the past few weeks, since I felt so out of control in the playground with the kids, I vowed never to be without something with which to cut myself. I realized that a knife or scissors were too big, so I bought a packet of razor blades and stashed one away in the pencil case in my school bag and another in my bedroom. Knowing they are there makes me feel calm; I know that I'm in con-trol of the pressure building inside me. I have the means to cut if I need to, and that makes me feel better.

Looking at Dad now, sitting awkwardly in his wheelchair, angry yet looking up at me — which feels wrong — I feel the tension inside me rise. I want to scream but I can't. How come his first words to me, after I've been so worried about him, are to put me down? I can't allow myself to cry, so I turn around and walk out.

I sit on the wall opposite the police car and within a few minutes Evan comes out. He puts a hand on my shoulder and I don't brush him off.

"Marsha," he says gently, "I'm worried about you. You haven't spoken to Miss Tina and I think you need to."

I look away, trying not to cry.

"Will you talk to me?"

I shake my head. "What's the use? You can't change my family. They blame me for everything and I try so hard to make things right."

"I can see that," he says.

I turn around to face him.

"You can?"

"Yes, I can. The problem isn't you; it's the way your parents communicate. I'm worried about you, Marsha. Are you still cutting?"

I look away again.

"Marsha?"

I shrug and say, "I can't help it."

"Y'know I can't let this go on. You know that, don't you?"

"What d'you mean?" I ask, with panic bubbling up inside me.

"If I know that you're harming yourself, I have to tell someone. It's my job. I'm a mandatory reporter."

"What's that?" I think.

"In my job, if I know that someone is hurting themselves or others, I *have* to report it. If I don't, I could get into trouble."

I look at him and I can feel my jaw tense.

"Don't, okay? Just don't say anything. You'll make things ten times worse for me if you tell anyone." I feel panic race through me. I couldn't bear it if everyone knew.

"Please, will you talk to Miss Tina?"

"I can't. There's nothing to say."

"Do you feel suicidal?" he asks.

I shake my head. No, I don't feel suicidal. I don't cut myself in order to end my life, I do it to get rid of the pressure building inside me, in order to feel something, *anything*. I do it because it's become a habit. I think I'm addicted to it in the same way Mom's addicted to alcohol.

"No, I don't feel suicidal."

The fact that he could ask me tells me that he has no clue about what's going on inside me. If I'd wanted to kill myself, I'd have done it quickly so that I didn't feel any pain. He's stupid. I want to feel pain so that I can actually feel *something*.

I could never kill myself because the kids need me. As I think it, it dawns on me... even though my mom treats me really badly, and my dad has just ripped into me after I haven't seen him for ages, I think *they* both need me too, if only to have someone to pick on. I hate my thoughts because, somewhere deep inside me, I realize that there's no escape for me. I can't opt out through suicide — and wouldn't because of the kids — but that leaves me abandoned, at the mercy of Mom, Grandma and Dad's anger. As the realization comes over me, I'm desperate to go inside and find the razor hidden in my room; I need to cut myself. I need to release the pressure inside me, for it's so bad that I think my head might explode any minute.

"Well, if you ever feel that way, do you promise to call me, or someone else?"

"Yes," I say, lying because I'm desperate to get rid of him.

He seems satisfied and drives off. He's a fool.

I go back into the house and head straight upstairs, ignoring everyone. I lock my door, but within seconds the kids are yanking on the door handle. I ignore them because I'm desperate to cut. I lift the corner of my mattress and there it is, wrapped in a tissue. It's a little parcel. The tissue makes it bigger than it is and stops it from getting lost in my bed. A thought flashes into my head; the razor is wrapped in the same way Mom used to wrap my teeth when they fell out. She wrapped them in tissue so that the tooth-fairy could find them. There seems to be something nasty about thinking of cutting and the tooth-fairy all in the same thought.

My heart's racing and I'm sweating. I have to cut, and I ignore the kids demanding to come into my room. They fade away as I hold the razor and try to find new skin. It's hard, though, as my forearms are criss-crossed with angry scars, all at different stages of healing. Every one of them is a reminder of the pain I can't express. The blade hovers above my arm. I gasp as I see the blood spring into life in lines across my arm. My heart races when I see the blood, but as stress pours out of me, my heart slows.

Eventually the kids' yelling at my door seeps into my consciousness. I blot the blood and press hard to stop the bleeding. I slip my thumbs into the hole in each cuff to hide what I've done and open the door.

"Why wouldn't you let us in?" Casey asks innocently.

"No reason," I lie, basking in the sense of relief the pain in my forearm gives me.

I look at their sweet faces and I feel ashamed. They're so trusting. If they were grown, they'd be disgusted at my behavior. My thoughts make me feel worse about myself and I can't look them in the eye. I act... it's all I seem to do, and it's all I seem to be good at.

"Hey, you guys, let's go and make dinner."

They follow me downstairs and I stay in the kitchen fixing dinner. I don't want to deal with Mom, Grandma and Dad. I can hear them talking. Mom's quiet but occasionally I hear her let out a sob. I struggle with the thought that I don't blame her. The sight of Dad with no legs makes me want to sob, too. Grandma sounds anxious, as if she's desperate to keep the conversation flowing. She asks him how it was in Basra.

"How d'you think?" Dad says scathingly, as if he thinks she's a piece of rubbish. "Don't you know that loads of men were killed in that place? I saw it every day. I saw women and children killed or maimed like me. No legs, no arms. Why d'you ask me such a thing?"

Grandma sounds flustered. "I was interested, that's all."

Dad's being hateful. "So, why are you here?" he asks, ignoring Mom, who cries and then blows her nose, waiting for someone to ask her what's the matter, but no one asks.

I put steaks on the grill and listen as best I can over the noise I'm making. Grandma sounds very flustered and Dad sounds angry. His tone twists my stomach; I *know* that tone of voice... he's angry, and he's determined to make everyone feel as bad as he feels, if not worse.

Although I'm glad my dad's alive, and home, I feel afraid. He's more angry than Mom and Grandma put together, and I don't think I can cope with having him join forces with them.

I fix the dinner as Grandma tries to avoid Dad's recriminations. I didn't know she had such self-control, and I'm annoyed when I realize she's able to turn her feelings on and off at will. I hate how I'm feeling, but I have no respect for her.

"Get me a drink, Marsha," Dad demands from the other room. "And then take me outside."

"D'you want coffee or a soda?" I ask.

He looks at me as if I'm a fool.

"Whisky."

I bite my tongue and don't say, "I will if Mom and Grandma have left any."

As I pour it, he picks on me.

"Why are you wearing your sleeves like that? You've ruined that tee-shirt by making holes in the cuffs."

I think quickly. "It's the fashion, Dad," I say.

"Well, it's stupid."

I hand him the glass of whisky and wheel him out into the back yard, thinking, "No, it's not stupid, it's necessary."

Casey comes running over to us with the broom-stick in his hands.

"Do you want to march?" he asks innocently.

Dad drains his glass and tells me to get him another. As I go back into the house, I hear him tell Casey to go away and leave him alone. I feel bad for Casey; he's just a little kid. He's trying to please Dad.

Mom and Grandma pour themselves a glass of whisky and I feel a flash of panic that there won't be enough for Dad.

"Dad wants another," I say quickly.

They look at each other and Grandma says, "I

better go and buy some more."

I guess they'd have asked me to go if I were older. I drain the bottle into Dad's glass and take it back out to him.

Shelley stands in front of him and says, "What's happened to your legs? Where are they?"

He takes a long swig from the glass, and I pray that he doesn't ask for another one until Grandma gets back. I tell the kids to go and play.

I feel awkward and scared that he'll bite my head off, but I say, "I'm glad you're back, Dad. It's been awful since you left."

He scowls at me. "Perhaps if you'd been more helpful your mother wouldn't have had to get on you so much. Honestly, Marsha, I was counting on you to help your mother... you know how she is. You've let me down."

A tear rolls down my face. I don't know what to say. If I stand up for myself, he'll just say I'm arguing, so I say nothing. I can't win.

"Don't you know what I've been through? It's been hell. I've seen things that no human being should have to see... bodies blown to bits. No one knows what war is like; it's hell on earth. You have to focus totally on what you're doing, because if you lose concentration, this can happen." He points to his stumps. "D'you know how many letters I got from your mother telling me how bad you've been? Do you? Every couple of days I'd get a new one with the latest thing you'd done, or not done. She told me that the kids were almost abducted."

"That wasn't my fault," I cry.

"Be quiet!" he orders, and I fall silent.

"D'you know what a worry it's been to me knowing that you've caused so much trouble while I've been gone? I've been distracted... worrying," he starts to slur. "You can't stay focused if you're worrying about everyone at home."

"It's not my fault," I cry. "I've tried to take care of everything since..."

"Be quiet," he snaps and the sentence dies on my lips.

He drains his glass and stares directly at me. He jabs a finger at me and says, "You can only stay safe in a war if you're not worried about your family at home, and I was worried all the time."

He grabs my arm and I wince with pain, praying that my new cuts won't leak through my sleeve.

"Get me another drink."

To my relief Grandma comes through the front door just as I come through the back one, and I ask her to pour Dad a drink.

"Take it to him," she says. "Perhaps it'll make him feel better."

Grandma fills it to the top and I take the glass out to him, concentrating, trying not to spill it.

He takes a deep gulp and says, "Where was I? Oh yeah. You can only stay safe in a war if you're not worried about your family at home. How d'you think it made me feel to read your mother's letters saying that you were causing so much trouble? I was so worried that I couldn't stay focused."

He takes another mouthful of whisky and then turns on me, grabbing my arm again.

"If I hadn't been so worried about what was going on at home, I wouldn't have lost my legs."

He cusses at me badly and I pull my arm away. The pain in my arm is nothing compared to the pain in my heart. He's blaming me for him losing his legs. How? Why? It's so unfair. A sob escapes me and I run away from him and ignore the kids calling after me.

It's too much to bear and I run upstairs, desperate to get away from him. I slam my bedroom door and lock it. My heart hammers in my chest and my head spins badly. I must be the most evil person who ever lived if the things my dad's saying are true. The pressure inside me is unbearable and there's only one thing I can do.

I lift the mattress up again and find the razor. I don't care this time about finding fresh skin. The pressure is so great that I take the razor and, driven by anger and injustice, I slice harder than I usually do over my left wrist.

Blood leaps along the line and I watch it, barely noticing the pain. I blot it with tissue but it won't stop bleeding. I hear the kids yanking my door handle, calling at me to open the door.

I'm scared. Instinctively I know that I've hurt myself badly, and I'm going to have to come out of my room. I don't want to, though, because I don't want the kids to be scared, but when the bleeding seems to get worse and I feel light-headed, I have no choice. I wrap a towel around my wrist as tightly as I can, and with a forced smile on my face, I open the door.

"We're hungry," the kids say together, and instantly I feel guilty. I follow them downstairs where I can smell the steaks burning on the grill, and as I walk into the kitchen, my head swims, and the last thing I hear as I fall to the floor is the sound of Shelley and Casey screaming.

Chapter Five

I awaken in a bed that's not my own. I groan. Where am I?

Someone comes up to my bed and, even though my head is foggy, I realize where I am. Miss Tina pats my hand. I must be at Beach Haven.

"What happened?" I murmur.

"You passed out because you'd lost a lot of blood. The ambulance brought you here. Sweetheart," she says, "I wish you'd been able to come to me and talk about it."

"He blamed me for losing his legs," I mumble.

She frowns. "What?"

Miss Tina helps prop me up against my pillows. My arms hurt and I feel really dizzy. Something above me catches my eye... it's a bag of blood that's attached to a line into my right arm.

"What d'you mean?" she asks me again.

"My dad just got back from Iraq. He lost both

his legs. It was a suicide bomber. He blamed me. He said that Mom had written telling him that I was causing trouble and he couldn't stay focused, so he lost his legs."

Miss Tina looks outraged.

"What! That's ridiculous."

I start to cry because for once someone can see what I'd prayed was true; all this was madness.

I find it hard to stop crying because finally I can tell someone what's been going on in our house.

"I did everything I could to take care of the kids, and Mom, even though she was so mean. She lost it the moment Dad left to go to Iraq. I promise you, I did try my best."

"Hush," Miss Tina says, "I know what's been going on in your house, okay?"

I look at her as my nose runs and tears stream down my face.

"Evan?" I ask.

She nods.

"He's a good man, and he has been worried about you for weeks. So have I."

Miss Tina walks to the end of my bed and picks up a chart. She walks over to the bag of blood hanging above me and peers at it, then writes something down on the chart. She takes my blood pressure and writes that down too. Then she sits on the edge of my bed.

"Listen, sweet girl, you're going to be fine.

You're here at Beach Haven and we're going to help you. We're hopefully going to help your parents, too, if they'll let us. We're going to help you to understand why you cut yourself, and we're going to help you beat the addiction."

I shiver. Addiction sounds like being an alcoholic or a drug addict, and I'm neither. But then I remember my thoughts several weeks ago when I was desperate to have something next to me so that I could hurt myself if I needed to. I remember thinking that perhaps I was just like my mom who needed something to help her cope when she felt bad.

"Cutting can be an addiction," Miss Tina says, seeing the puzzled look on my face. "C'mon, it's late. Time to go to sleep."

She helps me slide down the pillows and get comfortable, and she pats me on the shoulder. "I'll be coming in to check on you throughout the night. Sleep tight."

I awaken to the sound of a radio. I listen, waiting for someone to come into my room. I don't have to wait long.

An aide comes in.

"Hey girl, how're you doin'? Sleep okay?"

She chatters about her new car and how she hopes the seagulls won't poop on it.

"Seagulls?"

She tells me that Beach Haven is right by the beach as she helps me out of bed. I'm relieved that the bag of blood is gone and my right hand is free.

"Listen! Can you hear the seagulls screeching?"

I cock my head to one side and, yes, I can hear them.

"See," she says, "There's loads of them all hovering above my car. They'll hit it, I know they will. If I didn't know better I'd think that they were pooping on purpose; having a competition to see who can hit my car the most." She giggles and so do I.

She checks the stitches in my wrist and helps me take a shower. When I'm done, she tells me to get back into bed.

"Miss Tina says you've got to rest today, and tomorrow you can join the other kids here and work on your problems, okay?"

I feel dizzy and I'm glad to get back into bed. The room looks like a hospital but the sounds I can hear don't. I can hear kids shouting out to each other, laughing, and the radio is now blaring.

The day goes by in a blur as I drift in and out of sleep. Miss Tina checks on me during the day, and when it's dark outside she says I can transfer to my own room. She tells me that the room I'm in now is only used when kids need nursing care.

I follow her up a wide spiral staircase and along a corridor.

"This is your room, Marsha."

She walks over to the window and opens it. "The

ocean is so beautiful and soothing," she says.

She takes my hands and looks at the criss-crosses on my arms and says, "Sleep well, sweet girl. Tomorrow you're going to work on this and beat it, okay?"

In the morning I shower and feel anxious, not knowing what to do. I can hear kids everywhere. An aide knocks on my door.

"Time for breakfast," she says and walks with me down the spiral staircase and along a corridor. We stop outside a room that has a sign above it saying, "Dining Room."

She opens the door and I all but hide behind her; I'm afraid.

"Morning everyone, this is Marsha. Show her where everything is, okay?"

There are about twelve kids my age sitting around tables. All of them look my way and smile. Some wave. One girl stands up and comes over to me.

"Hi, I'm Macy. I'll show you what to do. Are you hungry?"

I nod. "Yes, I'm starving."

She shows me where to fill my plate, and as she points to the eggs and cheese, pancakes and syrup, I notice her arms — they're scarred with criss-cross lines. I'm aware that there's something different about me and her. I'm ashamed of my wounds and scars, yet she seems indifferent to them. It's almost as if they aren't there, for she doesn't care what I think about them.

I sit opposite her and she introduces the other three girls at the table.

"This is Poppy, Leisha and Candy," she says, pointing to each of them.

Poppy and Leisha have their thumbs anchored through their cuffs, but Candy's wearing a tee shirt and her arms have angry red criss-crosses all over them. She sees me looking.

"It took me a long time to be able to face what I've done to myself. I'm not proud of it, but I *am* proud of the progress I've made here at Beach Haven."

I seriously doubt that I'll ever be able to wear anything other than long sleeves again.

After we've cleaned our teeth and made our beds, I follow the girls downstairs towards a door that has a sign over it saying, "Group Room." There's a semicircle of chairs and Miss Tina sits in front next to a flipchart.

When everyone's quiet she says, "Welcome, Marsha. We're glad you're here."

My face flushes and I look at the floor.

Miss Tina carries on talking. "I expect you think that I'm going to lecture you about self-harming, but I'm not. What I'm going to do is to teach you about your personality so that you can understand why you feel the need to hurt yourself. I'm going to show you how to cope with the pressures that drive you to cut, and to be able to keep yourself safe in the future."

She gets up and starts to draw a rectangle and then divides it horizontally into five parts. She draws a head on the top of the rectangle and gives it a silly smile. Some of the girls giggle. Then she draws two arms at the side and two legs at the bottom. We're straining our heads to see as she writes something in each of the five parts of the rectangle. When she finishes, she sits down.

"This figure represents every human being's personality. When you look in the mirror, you just see yourself as being one whole entity, but everyone's personality is made up of five very separate parts. Have a look at them."

I read what Miss Tina has written.

The "Controlling Me"
The "Nurturing Me"
The "Thinking Me"
The "Modified Me"
The "Spontaneous Me"

The "Controlling Me"
The "Nurturing Me"
The "Thinking Me"
The "Modified Me"
The "Spontaneous Me"

I look at the other kids, and they look as blank as I do.

Miss Tina says, "To be whole and emotionally healthy, we need all five parts of your personality to be fully operational. We need to be able to use each part of ourselves at the appropriate time and in an appropriate situation. A well-balanced person has roughly the same available 'energy' in each part of their personality, ready to respond appropriately to different situations. Difficulties arise when we use the wrong part of ourselves for the particular situation."

I glance around again, still not really understanding what she's saying.

Miss Tina says, "From the moment of birth and during childhood, these five parts of the personality develop, and how four of the parts of you develop will depend a lot on your family and how they raised you. Those four parts can be used positively or negatively depending upon what you've learned in your families. Only the 'Thinking Me' part of yourselves is independent of how you were treated as a child."

She smiles at us.

"The 'Thinking Me' is like a computer inside your head. It works stuff out. You feed it information, as much as you can, and it makes decisions based on that information. You are functioning from your 'Thinking Me' right now because you're listening to what I'm saying and trying to make sense of it. I'm functioning from my 'Thinking Me,' too, as I'm giving you information. When you ask someone a question and expect an answer, you are using your 'Thinking Me.' When you read, study, write or learn, or you're assertive and ask for what you want or need, you're using this part of yourself."

Candy speaks out. "But how do you know when you're using this part of yourself?"

Miss Tina says, "The easiest way to identify whether someone is functioning from their 'Thinking Me' is to imagine news reporters. They are calm, their tone of voice is even and they impart information in an honest way."

"Oh, okay, that makes sense," Candy says, nodding as she's thinking.

"Because this part of you is not influenced by your past, it can't be used positively or negatively. It's merely the part of you that processes information and makes decisions based on evaluating all the facts. If you're unable to function from your 'Thinking Me,' you'll get yourself into a whole heap of trouble," Miss Tina says, smiling at us.

She stands up and walks to the flipchart, removing the top sheet of paper.

"Listening to the words people use can help you decide which part of themselves they're functioning from. Someone who's using his 'Thinking Me' will use words like…"

She writes on the flipchart.

What
When
Why
Where
How
Specifically
Precisely
Exactly
Basically
Essentially
Actually

"These words seek information, or they may be used when trying to explain something. These are the types of things you'll hear when two people are functioning from their 'Thinking Me.'"

What time will you be home tonight?
I'll be back by eight o'clock.
What would you like for dinner?
Can we have pizza, please?
I think it's time I got a hair cut.
Why? Do you like it short?
How much does that jacket cost?
It's $30, but the one over there is only $20.
Do you think I look good in blue?
Yes, you do, but I also like you in green.

What's your opinion of that day care program?
I'm not sure; I like some parts but other parts worry me.
I had such an awful day; the car broke down and I was late for work. I had to work late to make up for it. How was your day today?
My morning was good but this afternoon was awful.

"Can you see that when people use their 'Thinking Me,' they are exchanging information, asking questions and answering them? They are giving their opinion calmly after careful consideration and listening respectfully to the other person."

I nod. I get it. So do the other kids.

"Okay, let's look at the other four parts of your personality that depend a lot on how you were raised. Let's start with your 'Controlling Me.' When you've told your younger brothers and sisters, or your pet, what to do, have you ever thought that you sound just like your mom and dad?"

"Yes," Poppy laughs. "I sound just like my mom, and my little sister sounds like her, too, when she spanks her teddy bear."

Miss Tina laughs. "She's using her 'Controlling Me.' This part of yourself is concerned with taking control of others or the environment. Whether you use it positively or negatively will depend upon what you've learned from the adults in your life as a child — people like your parents, grandparents, aunts and uncles, teachers, priests and pastors. If people use this part of themselves positively, they'll be concerned with safety. But if they use it negatively, it's because they're irritated with others and want them to go away, or are trying to put them down. They may still be controlling, but they won't be concerned with safety."

She stands up again and goes to the flipchart.

"The type of words people would say if they're using their 'Controlling Me' in a positive way, are..."

Should
Shouldn't
Mustn't
Forbid
Right now
Ought to
Now
Quit
Stop it
Don't
That's enough
You can't

"The person's tone of voice will be firm, to the point, it may be stern and direct. You may be told what to do, but you won't feel shamed.

"But if people use their 'Controlling Me' in a negative way, the words they use will have an 'edge' to them. They'll sound persecutory, as if they are making a value judgment. The kind of words you'll hear are..."

Disgusting
Shocking
Outrageous
Ridiculous
Stupid
Duty
Contemptible
Intolerable
Disgraceful
Shameful
Scandalous

"The person's tone of voice may sound irritated, persecutory, angry, spiteful, scornful, shaming or picking fault. They may nag or lecture at you. You may still be told what to do, but you'll feel picked on, shamed and powerless. You'll feel small and bad."

"That's how I feel when my mom speaks to me," Leisha says sadly.

"I'm sorry," Miss Tina says.

I'm thinking hard as Miss Tina explains it all to us, and I venture to speak out.

"That's how I feel, too. My mom and grandma

make me feel really bad when they talk to me; so does my dad."

Miss Tina looks sad and shakes her head. "I hate that for you."

I shrug.

Several other kids say that their parents put them down.

"They're using their 'Controlling Me' in a negative way. Every parent needs to put in rules for their children, but they shouldn't belittle them in the process," Miss Tina says. "They probably learned their behavior from their own parents. This is how behaviors and attitudes are passed down from generation to generation. It's not good, but that's how it happens. Still, now that you know all this, you can change the way you interact with people, and then you won't pass these behaviors down to your children."

I feel horrified. I want to learn anything and everything I can so that I don't behave like my parents and grandma. Never!

Miss Tina stands up, walks towards the picture she first drew, and points to the next part of our personalities.

"This next part of yourself is called the 'Nurturing Me,' and it's the part of you that takes care of others. This can also be used positively or negatively. The kind of things people say using this part of their personalities positively are..."

Can I help you?
Are you feeling okay today?
Can you manage with that?
Here, let me take that for you.
Would you like my seat?
Let me get the door for you.
Would you like a back rub?
Would you like a cool drink?
You look tired; take a break.
Are you hungry?
Good job.

"Their tone of voice would be gentle and concerned. The difference between people using their 'Nurturing Me' in a positive or negative way is this. When it's used it in a positive way, it *enables* others to grow, to learn and become independent. But when people use it in a negative way, they *disable* others and make them feel useless. It happens when they do something for someone that they could do for themselves, or when they take over and make the other person feel stupid. Their tone of voice would sound exasperated, impatient, patronizing and condescending."

"My dad's like that," a boy says.

"Really, Greg?"

"Yeah. I wanted him to help me fix my bike, but he got mad and did it himself. I felt stupid."

Other kids say the same.

Miss Tina holds up her hand to silence us. "Can you see that using these parts of yourself in a positive way is good, but using them in a negative way is damaging?"

"So why would people use those parts of themselves in a negative way. After all, no one would like them. I wouldn't want to be around someone who's mean," Poppy says.

"Because it's what they've learned in their families. It's as if we soak up everything in our families like a sponge, the good and the bad. Unless you get the opportunity to learn a new way of being, you'll think it's the right way, and the only way, to behave."

"That's bad," Greg says, "but I understand what you mean because my dad thinks he's right all the time, and his way is the only way."

Miss Tina listens as kids call out. I look around, and not one says that their parents use their "Controlling Me" or their "Nurturing Me" in a positive way. That's sad. I wonder whether we'd be sitting here with angry criss-crosses on our forearms if they had.

Miss Tina breaks into my thoughts.

"Okay, settle down." Then she laughs and says, "Okay, who can tell me which part of my personality was I using just then?"

Candy calls out, "Your 'Controlling Me.'"

"Very good. Positively or negatively?"

"Um, positively."

"Because?"

"Because you were trying to take control of the environment, of us."

"Did it make you feel bad or ashamed?" Miss Tina asks.

"No. Not at all."

She beams. "Oh, you're so smart. Okay, the next part of your personality is called the 'Modified Me,' and it's the part of you that has to change in order to be accepted by those around you. We all need to fit into our families, then our schools, and as we grow up, into society. To do that we have to modify our true selves and our wants. Every human being wants his own way but has to learn to cope with waiting or with frustration. Small children learn that if they show good manners, they're more likely to get their needs met. They learn that if they're nice to people, others will usually be nice to them in return. If humans didn't learn to adapt to other people around them, they'd be selfish and self-centerd, caring only about getting their own needs met, and no one else's. We'd be like lions fighting over a carcass — just out for ourselves.

"So we need to learn how to adapt to other people's needs and to wait our turn. When we do this, we are using our 'Modified Me' in a positive way. We learn how to interact well with other people, use good manners, wait our turn, stand in line, and to put other people first. These things help us to be good citizens.

"But what happens if you live in a family where things go terribly wrong? How would someone adapt in that type of family? Here are some ways in which they may adapt in order to survive."

She walks around and hands us a piece of paper, and as I read I get goosebumps on my arms.

If I'm good and quiet, perhaps I won't get beaten.
If I try to be perfect, maybe Mom and Dad will
  love me.
If I'm strong and try really hard, then maybe
  Dad won't leave, or Mom won't drink and
  tell me it's my fault.
If I try to please them in every way, maybe
  they'll love me and I won't be so scared.
If I get fat, maybe Dad won't come to my room
  tonight.
If I hold my feelings in, perhaps no one'll
  notice me; then they'll leave me alone.

I swallow hard and want to cry.

"Adapting, or modifying, yourself in these ways is wrong, of course, but it may help you survive living in an abusive family. I'm so sad if any of you have had to modify yourselves in such drastic ways."

Macy speaks out. "That's how it is for me at home; I tried to be perfect so that they'd love me. Didn't work, though." She sounds angry and sad all in one.

Poppy says, "I tried to please everyone in my family, hoping that they'd love me, but it didn't do any good."

I want to say something, but I'm so close to tears that I don't dare. I want to say that I hold my feelings in so that my parents and grandma won't notice me, in the hopes that they'll leave me alone. It doesn't work, though. They just continue picking on me, and I don't know what to do with all my feelings. As I think it, I know it's a lie. I *do* know what I do with all the feelings inside me; I cut and let them out that way.

Miss Tina shakes her head over and over as everyone says something. "My heart hurts for you all," she says sadly.

Gradually silence falls over the group. She looks around at us.

"Are you okay to carry on?"

We say, "Yes."

"Because human beings and parents aren't perfect, they make mistakes, and it's a sad fact that *every* child learns to adapt to the negative things in their families. I'm not talking about the things you've just talked about; no child should have to endure abuse. I'm talking about the everyday mistakes that parents make because there's no rulebook showing people how to be parents. It's these mistakes that make children adapt and modify themselves in order to get their needs met, because they don't believe they can get them met in a clear and honest way.

"Have you seen the child that flashes her eyes at her dad, and he just falls over to give her what she wants? She doesn't do it when she's with her mom. She's learned to use her 'girliness' to get her own way. What about the child who sees his hospitalized brother get all his parents' attention? He learns that in order to get the same attention as his brother, he has to be sick and will pretend to have stomach aches or head aches until he believes they're real. Some kids throw a tantrum to get what they want. They are using their 'Modified Me' in a negative way. They may get their needs met initially, but ultimately using this part of themselves negatively will damage them.

Miss Tina walks around the semicircle of chairs again and hands out another paper.

"This is the most damaging part of a person's personality, this and the 'Controlling Me' used negatively. These two parts of yourself, used negatively, will hurt you and everyone else you come into contact with. If you believe that you function from these parts of yourself in a negative way, you must learn how to change, so that you can be healthy. If you can face these things about yourself, you will stop the legacy being passed on to the next generation. How awesome is that?" she says, smiling.

She hands me a paper.

"This paper shows lots of the types of behaviors that children learn in order to get their own way. They're not being true to themselves, they're adapting, modifying themselves. They are..."

Overly anxious
Overly competitive
Crying excessively
Testing limits
Making poor eye contact
Complaining excessively
Being hostile
Stubborn
Fidgety
Sarcastic
Hysterical
Having the last word
Isolating self
Being aggressive
Pleasing others
Always saying "yes"
Being the class clown
Being somatic
Sucking up
Cussing
Being passive aggressive
Escalating behavior
Lying
Manipulative
Bombarding

Hyperverbal
Dramatic
Sulking
Being defensive
Arguing
Moaning
Suspicious
Irritable
Solemn
Whiny
Sighing loudly
Pouting
Yelling
Placating
Criticizing
Teasing
Pleading
Begging
Being gamy
Being bitchy
Gossiping
Self-harming
Acting dumb
Disrespectful
Showing off

Arrogant　　　　　　　　　*Snobby*
Muttering under breath　　*Being loud*

Miss Tina goes back to her chair and lets us read. It's bad. As I read, I try to think whether I do these things. I guess I sulk. Sometimes I'm irritable, and I know I can be sarcastic. I remember telling Mom that if she weren't so hung over every morning, she might know what her kids were doing that day. I feel embarrassed.

"Can anyone think of a time when you wouldn't have learned any of these things?" Miss Tina asks us.

I look at Candy and then Poppy, and I feel stupid because I can't think of the answer.

"When you're a newborn baby," Leisha says.

Miss Tina claps her hands and says, "Oh, Leisha, well done. That's exactly right. A newborn baby doesn't show any of those behaviors. Every one of these behaviors has been *learned*. They've been learned because children couldn't get their needs met properly in their families, and they had to resort to 'underground' tactics. Babies don't start out that way, they learn those behaviors."

My head is spinning as I take in everything Miss Tina's saying and try to apply it to myself. What have I learned in order to fit in to my family? I feel a bit sick.

Miss Tina stands.

"We've covered a lot, so let's take a break."

Chapter Six

I follow the others towards a living room that is full of squashy armchairs and sofas. In the corner of the room is a fridge. The kids grab an ice-cold soda and Macy hands one to me.

"Let's go outside," she says.

I follow her and the others out onto the playground, and we sit on benches.

Candy says, "Well, now I know what's wrong with my older sister. She's *so* histrionic and dramatic; she's functioning from her 'Modified Me' in a negative way." She laughs. "Can you imagine me saying that to her? She'd freak and tell me I was a smart-mouth. It's almost worth doing just to get a rise out of her."

"Oh ho," Leisha laughs. "Now look who's coming from their 'Modified Me' in a negative way; you're instigating."

I can't help it; I laugh, too.

"That was some list of behaviors; I think most people would do one or two of them at some time," Poppy chips in.

"Yeah, but Miss Tina said that *every* child adapts to their parents' mistakes in some way, even if it's only in small ways. So I guess everyone can function from their 'Modified Me' in a negative way sometimes," Macy says wisely.

That makes me feel a bit better because I *know* I can operate from my "Modified Me" in a negative way sometimes.

"Don't you think it's scary that all this time we've been functioning from parts of ourselves that we didn't even know we had?" I say. "It feels as if I've been wandering around with a blindfold on, stumbling about trying to get things right but not having a clue how to go about it."

The others nod.

"Miss Tina said that we'll get ourselves into trouble if we use the wrong part of ourselves at the wrong time or in the wrong situation," Macy says. "So that's what I've been doing wrong," she jokes.

We all fall silent trying to work out what Miss Tina means.

Greg comes over to us and says, "Hey, don't stop talking just because of me."

Poppy slaps him playfully. "Nerd."

"Group was heavy," he says. "It kind of changes the way you see things."

"Yeah," we all say together.

We hang out until a bell rings, and I follow the kids inside to the Group Room.

Miss Tina's already there and waits until we sit quietly before starting to speak.

"Okay. We got as far as describing the types of behaviors you'd see when people function from their 'Modified Me' in a negative way. But what kind of words or tone of voice would help you identify it? This part of yourself is one of the easiest to identify."

She walks to the flipchart and starts to write.

"These are the types of things you'll hear someone say."

Oh, go on, please, let me.
You don't love me anymore, that's why you
    won't give it to me.
It's not fair.
See!
I told you so.
Well, excuse meeeee!
Whatever!
You said...

"The tone of voice is one of the easiest ways of identifying when people function from their 'Modified Me' in a negative way." She grins at us. "My favorite give-aways are whining, hysteria and sarcasm. People who sound like this are in their negative 'Modified Me.'"

She writes on the flipchart.

Whining	*Hysterical*
Pleading	*High-pitched*
Sarcastic	*Bragging*
Sounding shocked	*Spiteful*
Saying things for effect	*Sounding seductive*
Shouting	*Screaming*

"You can learn so much about people not only from the things they say but also from their non-verbal communication, their body language. Here's a list of behaviors and expressions that people might use if they were functioning from their negative 'Modified Me.'"

She hands each of us a paper.

Quick to anticipate others' needs
Frowning
Biting their lip
Smiling a lot, like their face is a mask
Sighing loudly
Overly concerned for the welfare of others
Hunched shoulders and they will be looking up
Being passive aggressive
Shrinking and subservient
Avoiding eye contact

Chin tucked down as if they don't matter
What is said doesn't match their non-verbal
*   communication*
Fighting and arguing
Flashing eyes seductively
Drawing attention to the self
Sulking
Going quiet for days
Looking like a little child
Trying to be cute, shy or timid
Acting dumb
Jutting out their chins
Rolling eyes
Rolling head in defiance
Raising a fist
Fix it for me; I'm weak and vulnerable
Daring others to challenge them

Miss Tina waits for a minute as we read and then starts to talk.

"These are just a few things to describe the behaviors that people functioning from their negative 'Modified Me' could use. The list is endless. When you become expert at watching people to see which part of themselves they're operating from, you'll discover other behaviors or expressions. These are just the basics."

Candy says what I'm thinking.

"It's awesome but a bit scary. It's like there's

no hiding place anymore. Now that you've told me about these parts of my personality, I can't kid myself about my behavior anymore or kid myself about my family's behavior either."

"Sorry," Miss Tina says, smiling, not at all remorseful. "Welcome to therapy. Therapy is about learning the truth, facing it, dealing with it and moving on. No one said that it was going to be easy."

"Yeah, but," Candy says, "I don't feel that it's bad, it's just mind blowing. I don't think I'll ever look at myself or anyone else in the same way again."

"Therapy!" Miss Tina says again, smiling.

I get the feeling that she's about to crack up laughing but she controls it, and as I think those thoughts, another pops into my head. "Is she functioning from her 'Controlling Me' to take charge of herself?"

Something slips into place in my mind; I know what Candy means, I'm analysing, too. I'm working stuff out. I'm not taking anything on face value anymore. I'm trying to understand what part of Miss Tina's personality she's functioning from. I feel a strange sense of excitement flow through me, even though part of it feels uncomfortable.

"Remember, our negative 'Modified Me' allows us to get what we want without caring about other people. We manipulate others and play 'mind games' to get what we want. It is damaging to other people, and although we may initially get what we want by using this part of ourselves, it will hurt us in the end. We won't be liked and others will see us as being 'unsafe,' or hard work to be around."

I feel shivers settle on me and I vow that no matter how hard I have to work to change, I'm not going to function from my negative "Modified Me."

The room is silent as we wrestle with our thoughts.

Miss Tina waits a while before walking to the page stuck to the wall that shows us our personalities. She seems to brighten and change.

"*This* is what I've been waiting to share with you. This is the part of you that will set you apart from other people. It'll show everyone how special you are.

"Think back to the questions I asked you about newborn babies. They have yet to learn the ways of their families. All they have is their raw, uncensored selves."

Miss Tina stands up and starts drawing on the flip-chart. It's a weird, rounded oblong shape. I watch, wondering what she's going to say next. When she's finished, she sits down.

"This is a picture of a human brain, a poor one at that. Sorry, I can't draw. You see this funnel shape at the back of the brain? Well, that's the brain stem and that's where the four core emotions live."

"What?" Greg asks.

Miss Tina draws another picture. She draws the head of a dog. Inside it she draws the same weird, rounded, oblong shape with the funnel pointing down.

"Look at the differences and similarities between these two brains. What do you see?"

"The human brain is bigger than the dog's brain at the top."

"Well spotted," Miss Tina says. "That part of the brain is called the cerebral hemisphere, and it's where all our conscious thoughts are. If someone could scan your brains as you're sitting here thinking, they'd see loads of activity in that part of the brain because you are thinking and taking in information. Dogs, or other mammals, don't have such big cerebral hemispheres. That's not to say that they don't think — they probably do, but at a simpler level. What other differences or similarities can you see between the two brains?"

Greg says, "They both have the same bottom bit of their brains."

"Yes, they both share the same 'brain stem.'"

"What?" several kids ask.

Miss Tina draws a line across each of the brains at the same level, and it's obvious that the brain stem is common to both.

"The four core emotions — happiness, sadness, anger and fear — live in this part of the brain. You've all seen your dog wag his tail when he's happy, whine when he's sad, growl when he's angry, and his hackles rise when he's afraid. He displays the same four core emotions that humans have, and that's because they come from the part of the brain that is common to all mammals."

"I'm confused. You've given us several handouts that show all kinds of feelings. How can you say that there are only four core emotions?" Greg asks directly.

"All the feelings identified in your handouts are products of these four core feelings. If you hunt hard enough behind any one of those feelings on your handouts, you'll find the four core emotions hidden beneath them."

"What d'you mean?" a kid asks.

"Well, feeling embarrassment is a learned feeling. No baby is born feeling embarrassed. Yet beneath the learned feeling of embarrassment is a feeling of fear — fear of being rejected."

"Oh."

The room's quiet. I struggle to see what my behaviors may be hiding. It's like a shot in the dark. I know I feel hostile towards my parents and grandma, so what's beneath that feeling? Suddenly it's obvious to me, and I hate it because it overwhelms me. My feelings of hostility are hiding my core feelings of sadness. I'm sad that my parents aren't there for me. I want to cry but I'm good at keeping my feelings in, so I don't.

Miss Tina stands up and points to the last part of ourselves, our "Spontaneous Me."

"This part of yourselves includes all four core emotions. It also includes any pain and hurt you may feel. It's about being *true* to yourself and others. But it's more than the four core emotions, much more. Imagine yourself as a baby. You laugh when you're happy, cry when you're sad, cling when you're scared and scream when you're angry. You are uncensored. You are who you really are before you start to learn to modify yourself, or adapt to your family.

"Babies show us exactly what they're feeling without hiding anything. They're spontaneous, which means that they react immediately to what they're feeling; if they're uncomfortable, hungry or in pain, they cry right away. They gurgle, giggle and babble when they're happy, splash about in their baths, having fun, without worrying about making a mess. The 'Spontaneous Me' is similar. It's the part of you that feels, that is spontaneous, creative and excited about living and about the things you're doing; it's the part of you that is real and honest. When you are doing something that makes you feel happy and excited, but it isn't harming you or others, you're functioning from your 'Spontaneous Me.'"

"I like this part," Leisha says.

Miss Tina smiles at her. "It's the best bit of our-selves, but sometimes a person's 'Spontaneous Me' has been squashed by his parents, who had theirs squashed by their parents, too. Look at the picture of your personalities. Look at the poor 'Spontane-ous Me' squashed under all the other parts."

She draws a little sad face in the "Spontaneous Me" part of the picture, and says, "You have to res-cue your 'Spontaneous Me' so that you can enjoy life and have fun.

"Let's look at the things someone would do if they used this part of themselves negatively. Us-ing this part of yourself means that you'll satisfy yourself, no matter what the consequences are. If you're in church and you need to pass gas and do so, you're using your 'Spontaneous Me' in a negative way. You want to satisfy yourself but in doing so you harm yourself... everyone looks at you and thinks you have no manners."

Some of the kids laugh and I want to, but I don't.

"That's what happens if you use your 'Spontane-ous Me' in a negative way. You gratify yourself, but in doing so, you hurt yourself. If you want to drink alcohol because it tastes good and takes away your inhibitions, or if you want to smoke pot because it chills you out, you're satisfying your urges, but you're hurting yourself."

We're all listening intently.

"When we were cavemen, we gratified ourselves in the same way animals do. C'mon, you know what I mean. You've all seen animals take what they want regardless of who's watching."

An image of a dog humping another on the kids' playground flashes into my head. Yes, animals *do* take what they want and don't care who's watching or what they think.

"Well, if people behave in the same way, they satisfy their urges... but the consequence to themselves will be bad."

"So, we should try hard not to function from any of the negative parts of ourselves," Greg says.

"Yes, that's what personal growth is all about; recognizing when we're functioning from the negative parts of ourselves and trying to change it. But therapy is also about being able to free this poor squashed part of yourself, the positive 'Spontaneous Me.'"

Miss Tina points to the picture of our personalities.

"Using your 'Spontaneous Me' in a positive way is like 'flowering' as God intended you to. It's like being *joyful*. When you're playing without any inhibitions, and laughing because something tickles you, you're functioning from your positive 'Spontaneous Me.'

"The most magical thing about this part of yourselves is that when you operate from it, people want to be with you. You draw people to you like a magnet. They want to be like you, and you help them to access their 'Spontaneous Me.' Isn't that wonderful? They like you because they can tell that you're being *real*. When you're showing your four core emotions — sadness, fear, anger and joy — they'll sense that you're being *real*."

She gives a little cough.

"Everyone wants to be in a loving relationship, but here's a little tip; the *only* way you will have true intimacy with another human being — and I'm not talking about sex — is when you can function comfortably in this part of yourself. That's why you have to work hard to be *real* and work through your issues."

I think about my mom and dad. They don't have true intimacy. As I think about all the things Miss Tina's taught us, it slides into place in my head. Neither my mom nor my dad uses their "Spontaneous Me" so how can they be close?

"Are there any special words that will help us identify when someone is using their positive 'Spontaneous Me'?" Macy asks.

Miss Tina walks to the flipchart and writes.

Cool
Wow
Awesome
Wheeeee!

Fab
Wicked
Great
I feel...

"You won't feel conned by someone functioning from their positive 'Spontaneous Me' and they'll sound authentic and real. They won't be playing any mind games."

Miss Tina rips off the page and sticks it to the wall. On the fresh page she draws a bar chart with five bars all the same height and beneath them she puts the initials, CM, NM, TM, MM and SM.

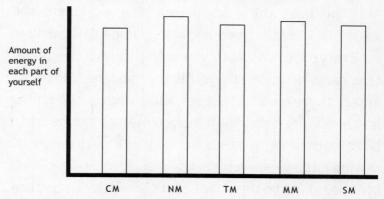

Amount of energy in each part of yourself

CM   NM   TM   MM   SM

"These five bars represent how much energy you have in the five parts of your personality. To be a well-balanced person who's emotionally healthy, you shouldn't use the parts of your personality negatively. You should have roughly the same amount of energy available in each of the five parts of yourself to use at the appropriate time."

"What d'you mean?" Leisha asks.

"Well, if you're sitting in a lecture at school, you need to be in your 'Thinking Me.' It wouldn't be appropriate for you to be in your 'Spontaneous Me,' being playful and having fun. But if you were at a party you'd want to be in your 'Spontaneous Me' rather than in your 'Controlling Me' telling everyone what to do. And if you were at church you'd want to be in your 'Modified Me' being quiet and respectful."

"Oh, I see," Leisha says. "That makes sense." Miss Tina asks if we understand everything she's told us, and we say, "Yes."

"The best thing about learning all this," she says, "is, now that you know it, you can't 'unknow' it. Every time you feel yourself slip into the negative parts of yourself, you'll feel yourself doing it, and that means you'll understand what's happening inside you. You can then make a better choice as to how to behave. It means that you can make real, lasting changes in yourself."

She points to the sheet of paper with the picture of our personalities, and says, "I want you to think about this; which part of yourself are you functioning from when you cut yourself?"

My stomach churns; I'd forgotten about it. Miss Tina said that she wasn't going to lecture us about cutting.

"Your negative 'Modified Me,'" Candy says.

"Could be," Miss Tina says. "Any other parts of yourself?"

I glance around the room and we all look at each other. I think really hard. I know it's not from my "Controlling Me" or my "Nurturing Me," neither can it be from my "Thinking Me." It has to be from my "Spontaneous Me," but how?

Greg says, "From your negative 'Spontaneous Me.' Didn't you say that if you give in to an urge even if it hurts you, you'd be functioning from your negative 'Spontaneous Me'?"

"Very good," Miss Tina says. "You're both right. It depends on why you're cutting. If you've become addicted to the rush you can feel when you cut, then you'd be functioning from your negative 'Spontaneous Me.' But if you cut because you can't let your feelings out any other way, then you're not being *real*, so you'd be operating from your negative 'Modified Me.' Either way, it's still damaging to you."

She picks up a pen and writes on the flipchart, "Why do people cut?"

"Call out everything you can think of, okay? Call out, even if it isn't why *you* do it."

We start to shout out and she writes frantically.

To make my body feel real.
To get rid of the anger I feel.
To cover the guilt I feel at not being good
*   enough.*

It distracts me from painful memories and feelings.

To have a mark outside that shows my pain inside.

To try and stop flashbacks.

To punish myself.

It makes me feel alive.

I feel in control of myself.

I can control other people.

I get attention.

Someone has to take notice of me.

It's a cry for help.

It makes my body unattractive.

It stops me from having to talk about my problems.

Helps me cope with stress.

It makes me feel safe.

It stops me from hurting other people.

It reduces the tension I feel.

I feel something rather than nothing.

It releases my pent-up feelings.

"Oh my, that's a lot of reasons. What feelings are common to all of these reasons for cutting?"

"Hurt and pain," Leisha says.

"And if your feelings are real, where will you find hurt and pain in the five parts of your personality?" Miss Tina asks, pointing to the picture stuck to the wall.

I answer. "In your 'Spontaneous Me.'"

"Yes, Marsha, well done."

My face flushes.

"Tell me, if you were to see a small child hurting and in pain, what part of yourself would you function from?"

That's easy. Images of Casey and Shelley flash into my mind.

"My 'Nurturing Me,'" I say.

"Yes, your 'Nurturing Me.' This is the part of you that will stop you from hurting yourself ever again. Marsha, come here."

I feel awkward, but I stand up and go over to her.

"I want you to draw your personality as a bar chart. How much energy do you have available in each of the five parts of your personality for yourself, not towards other people, but for yourself?"

"What d'you mean?" I ask, feeling stupid.

"How much energy do you have in each part of yourself to be able to influence your behavior?"

She hands me the pen and I start to draw. I make my "Controlling Me" fairly high as I keep control of myself pretty well. Then I think about not being able to stop myself from cutting, so I rub it out with my sleeve and make the bar lower. I go on to draw the amount of energy I have in my "Nurturing Me" that I use towards myself, and all I can draw is a slither half an inch high. I know I don't take care of me. My "Thinking Me" is higher because I'm always having to think ahead and hold things together at home. I try to stay focused on how much energy I have to spend on me, but it's hard; I don't usually think about *me*. I falter as I think about my "Modified Me." I have good manners, I know I do. That's positive. I please people... I don't know if that's good or bad. But I can be sarcastic when Mom picks on me and I know that's negative. I don't know how to draw it.

Miss Tina takes the pen and draws the bar representing my "Modified Me" and then shades in a proportion, saying, "You can separate out the amount of energy you have in this part of yourself into positive and negative."

She hands the pen back to me, and I draw a tall bar. I shade in half of it to represent the fact that, although I have good manners and I'm a good citizen, I can be sarcastic and not be *real* at times. I look at the space waiting for my "Spontaneous Me," and I get an urge to cry. What can I draw there? I feel frozen and everything seems to fade away. Tears start to fall down my face, and I'm barely aware of Miss Tina putting her arms around me and patting my shoulder.

When my sobs subside, she looks back at the bar chart.

"Marsha, draw how much energy you have in

your 'Spontaneous Me.'"

I shake my head. "I can't. There's nothing there. I can't feel anything; I can't play or have fun. I don't even know who I am."

Miss Tina sounds stern. "Oh, yes, you do. Your personality is made up of five parts and the only bit you're unacquainted with is your 'Spontaneous Me.' How many others in this room feel the same way?"

"Me."

"Me, too."

"And me."

All the kids call out.

"You will get to know this part of yourself while you're here at Beach Haven, but more importantly, you'll be able to rely on the one part of you that will keep you safe for the rest of your life, your 'Nurturing Me.'"

I go back to my seat as Miss Tina continues talking.

"What resources do you have in your personality that you could draw on to help you stop cutting yourselves?"

Macy says, "My 'Controlling Me' could *order* me to stop, but I don't know if I'd listen."

Poppy says, "I could use my 'Thinking Me' to work out the pros and cons of cutting myself, but I can't think straight when I'm about to cut."

Leisha says in a small voice, "I could try and let my core feelings out properly, instead of trying to keep them bottled up inside me, and then cutting because the pressure gets too bad. But I can't do that, it's too hard."

"What about your 'Nurturing Me'? How could that part of you help you to stop cutting?" Miss Tina asks.

We're silent until Candy says, "Um, could your 'Nurturing Me' try and take care of you?"

"Yes, definitely," Miss Tina says. "Let's look at why the other parts of you won't be so successful in stopping you from cutting yourselves. Macy, you already identified that you won't listen to your 'Controlling Me' if it should tell you to stop. That's because the urge to cut is so strong that it overrides any voice that tries to stop it. You'll 'dig your heels in,' so to speak, and be defiant. That means, you're more likely to continue cutting if you try to use this part of yourself to help you stop."

"What about your 'Thinking Me'?" Poppy asks.

"Well, as you just said, when you're stressed, it's almost impossible to think straight. So, even if you sit there and make lots of good plans, if you're stressed out, it's unlikely you'll be able to access the plan you've made to help yourself."

That makes sense to me because, when I need to cut, I'm not thinking at all.

"Leisha, what did you say?"

"I said that perhaps you could use your 'Sponta-neous Me' to let your real feelings out."

Miss Tina smiles at her and says, "I love it. You're so smart."

Leisha looks pained. "But I can't do it." She shrugs. "It's okay to say what you should do, but I can't *do* it."

"And d'you know why you can't do it?" Miss Tina asks.

Leisha shakes her head, and I don't know either.

"It's because you don't have access to your 'Nurturing Me.' If you're about to strip away your one coping mechanism, cutting, you need to be able to nurture yourself, to take care of the pain and hurt inside you. Your 'Controlling Me' won't do that, and neither will your 'Thinking Me.' Your 'Modified Me' may help you cover up your feelings for a while longer, but it won't help you become healthy. Only your 'Nurturing Me' will keep you safe and will help you recover from the hurt and pain you feel."

She walks away from the flipchart and sits down.

"Look at Marsha's bar chart. Bless her heart, she has virtually no energy in her 'Nurturing Me' or in her 'Spontaneous Me.'"

I feel mortified, and I look towards the flipchart where my bar chart is there for all to see.

Tears start to flow down my face, and even as I feel consumed with pain, I'm determined to learn. I'm going to learn how to access my "Nurturing Me" so that I can beat this. Yet as I think it, and my tears flow down my face, the urge to cut becomes unbearable.

Chapter Seven

"What are you feeling now?" Miss Tina asks me gently.

I can't answer, but she presses me.

I mumble. "I want to cut myself, and I feel scared because I haven't got anything to do it with."

"Thank you for being honest with us. Can you say why you want to cut?"

"Because I..." I can't think. "Because I feel as if I'm going to explode." I'm trembling. I feel as if my skin is going to rip open and I'm going to splatter the walls with my insides... a vile, horrible mess.

"You're feeling pent-up pressure because you don't know how to express your feelings. You *have* to learn another way to get rid of pent-up pressure other than cutting. I want you to scream."

"What?"

"I want you to scream," she says insistently.

"I can't."

"Yes, you can. Think of all the times you've wanted to scream at your mother. Think of all the times you've wanted to scream at your grandma but couldn't. Well, now you can. Scream."

I make a silly little noise and feel embarrassed.

"Go on, louder. Scream for all the times that they blamed you for everything."

I can't do it. I want to cry. I don't know how to get angry. I'm not allowed to at home.

"Macy, can you help Marsha? Can you show her how to let out pent-up pressure?" Miss Tina says.

Macy grins at us and says, "Oh, yeah," nodding her head. She stands and holds up her hands and does a little dance. The other kids laugh. I'm confused. They seem to be having fun when I'm falling apart. Then it dawns on me that perhaps they've done this before with other new kids.

Macy stands in front of me and takes my hands. "Are you ready? I'm loud," she says, grinning.

I nod. She takes a deep breath and opens her mouth. The noise is deafening. When she runs out of breath she takes another and screams again and again.

In between breaths she says, "C'mon," and I make a feeble attempt to open my mouth and yell. Poppy, Leisha and Candy jump up and join us, and they scream and scream. There's nothing else I can do but scream with them. I'd feel even sillier standing there in silence when they were screaming in my face. As I let myself scream, something starts to happen inside me. Images of Mom blaming me for Shelley and Casey getting lost flash into my head. I scream louder. Then I hear my dad blame me for him losing his legs, and I scream even louder until I'm making as much noise as the others. As my eyes widen and I glance around feeling strangely detached from my raw throat, I notice that the kids around us are laughing. The girls gradually stop screaming and they're laughing, too. They jump up and down and hug me. The other kids pat me on the back and tell me I did a good job.

Miss Tina hugs me and tells us to sit down.

"How d'you feel now?" she asks me.

"My throat hurts," I say meekly.

"I'm not surprised," she says, laughing. "That was some scream. I knew you could do it. 'Scream therapy' is wonderful. Mind you, you need to be in a safe place to do it... screaming in the superstore or a restaurant will get you locked up! Seriously, Marsha, how d'you feel inside?"

I think for a moment. I can't believe it; I feel better than I did five minutes ago. I tell her.

"And do you still feel that you have to cut yourself to get rid of the pressure inside you?"

I shake my head. "No, I don't. I need something for a sore throat, though," I say with a smile on my face.

"You've just learned another way of releasing

the tension inside you, a way that doesn't hurt you other than clear out your throat. 'Scream therapy' is awesome because it automatically taps into your feelings, even if you can't reach them any other way. It reveals your feelings to you. It's the first step to owning your feelings and getting them out. Once you're able to express them, you'll use *quieter* methods to cope with your feelings." Miss Tina grins at me. "But it's a great introduction to them, isn't it? They've been hidden for so long, so let's give them a welcome, one that you won't forget."

She lets us go and get a soda, and I'm glad. My throat is raw and I'm shaking, but as I pull the ring and take a swig, I realize that I feel calmer inside. I'm amazed.

When we take our seats again, Miss Tina asks me a question.

"Marsha, earlier you said that you were scared because you didn't have anything to cut yourself with. That's an interesting statement, and I want us to look at what it means. Can you say what you meant by it?"

I take another swallow from my can of soda to give me some thinking time. An image pops into my head from nowhere and I know what to say.

"One day I was so stressed that I was desperate to get away from my mom and grandma, that I took my little brother and sister to the playground. I wanted to cut myself, but because I didn't have something to do it with, I felt panic. I bribed the kids with candy to make them go home early so that I could be close to a knife."

I clear my poor raw throat. I feel ashamed telling these kids the things that I did, but they just look at me and nod, like they know where I'm coming from.

"It wasn't that I wanted to cut right then; it was knowing that I couldn't that bothered me. Being in the playground without anything to cut with freaked me out. After that, I was never without a razor blade."

Miss Tina says, "So, what you're saying is that having something to cut with in your possession at all times made you feel in control. Is that right?"

I think for a moment.

"Yes, but just because I had the razor blade with me didn't mean that I *would* cut, but not having it made me want to cut out of panic."

"What you're talking about is *control*," Miss Tina says. "And that's something that most cutters don't have in their lives. Cutting gives them a sense of control. Does that fit your situation?" she asks me.

Something clicks inside my head. I have no control at home.

"Yes, it made me feel safe somehow."

"So how do you feel now, without one?"

Everyone is looking at me, and I feel like a bug under a microscope. If I lie they'll know, but I'm not used to being honest and saying what I think.

"Anxious."

"Is there any pent-up pressure inside you that would make you want to cut?"

"No. I just got rid of it by screaming."

"So what's making you feel anxious?" Miss Tina asks kindly.

I shrug; I don't know.

"It's a habit. It's a learned feeling. In the past when you've had so many pent-up feelings inside you that you thought you might explode, having a razor blade on you gave you a sense of control and reduced your anxiety. You've become used to feeling anxious if you haven't got a razor on you, but you have no need to feel anxious if you don't have any pent-up feelings inside you. Do you?"

I shrug again.

"What you have to do now is to break the habit of feeling anxious."

"How?"

"By replacing it with something else every time you start to feel it."

"With what?"

"Let's think. Which part of yourself are you functioning from when you feel anxious?" she asks me.

I wrack my brain. Being anxious is a feeling, so it should be part of my "Spontaneous Me" but Miss Tina just said that it was a habit, so it can't be a *real* feeling. It must be my "Modified Me" being used negatively.

"My negative 'Modified Me,'" I say.

Miss Tina beams at me. "Awesome," she says. "You're so smart. Okay, so what other parts of your-self can you use to stop yourself from slipping into your negative 'Modified Me'?"

"Um, I could use my 'Controlling Me' to tell my-self to stop it and not to be so silly."

"That sounds persecutory, and telling someone that they're being silly is a value judgment. That's from your negative 'Controlling Me' and using that will hurt you. That won't help."

"Okay." I look at the picture of our personalities and take a guess. "Um, I could use my 'Nurturing Me' to tell myself that I'm okay and nothing bad is going to happen to me just because I don't have a razor on me."

"Very good. Could you use your 'Thinking Me' to help get rid of your 'anxiety habit'?"

"I guess. I suppose I could think it through and see that I don't have anything to be anxious about."

Miss Tina looks pleased with me. "And could you use your 'Spontaneous Me' to get rid of your 'anxi-ety habit'?"

I shake my head.

"You could laugh at it," she says. "Laughing at something scary takes away the fear. Every time you start to feel anxious, you could laugh at yourself and say, 'Oh, there I go again.' Would that help?"

"I guess."

"So every time your 'anxiety habit' starts to creep up on you, replace it by telling yourself that you're okay and nothing bad is going to happen to you, or laugh at it."

"Okay," I say, feeling determined to beat it.

"Marsha, I'm so proud of you," she says, and she comes over to me and gives me a hug.

"Okay, we're done for today," Miss Tina says. "Enjoy yourselves. Rest and grow."

The kids file out of the room and I follow them.

"What does she mean, 'rest and grow'?" I ask Macy.

"At Beach Haven we have to be totally honest with ourselves and each other so that we can 'grow,' but it's hard, and so we're given plenty of time to get used to it, 'to rest.' It's awesome, actually. It's scary at first because there's no hiding place; you have to be honest with yourself and everyone else, but once you get used to it, it feels amazing."

I feel a tinge of fear that's mixed with excitement. I want what these kids have. Suddenly I understand why Macy and Candy wear short sleeves. They're proud of their 'growth.'

I follow the kids and they head toward a classroom.

"It's cookout night," Poppy tells me. "We cook our own food. It's cool. I love barbecued ribs. We make the guys fix the fire outside and we make the salad."

"What?"

She giggles. "They build a fire on the beach, and when it's ready we take the meat out so that they can cook it. Here, wrap these potatoes in foil; then they can put them in the embers. They take a long time but they taste pretty good."

"Hello, Marsha," a lady comes over to me. "I'm Miss Cassie, your life skills teacher."

"Hi." She walks over to Leisha, looks over her shoulder and tells her she's doing a good job of chopping lettuce.

I wrap loads of potatoes, and Macy tells me to take them outside to the guys who are working on the fire.

They are huddled around something, and as I stumble across the sand, I see a wisp of smoke.

"Hey, Macy told me to give you these to put in the embers."

They're blowing frantically to keep the fire alive and don't answer me, so I leave the potatoes next to them and walk away.

"Thanks, Marsha," Greg calls out.

"Yeah, thanks," another guy says. "Hey!"

I turn around.

"What?"

"You scream well. My name's Franklin, by the way."

I feel flustered, and so I ignore him and go back inside to help the girls prepare the salad.

When I get back to the classroom, Miss Cassie hands me a knife and tells me to start slicing cucumbers. I start slicing, and as it dawns on me that I've got a knife in my hand, I look at Miss Cassie and she seems to know what I'm thinking.

"Are you surprised?" she asks. "Listen, Marsha. We trust you here. We trust that you will come and tell us if you can't control the urge to cut yourself. Everyone here wants to get better, so they don't betray that trust."

A wave of fear washes over me. I'm scared of the knife, and I put it down. I'm scared that I won't be able to control my urges. A tear rolls down my face.

"What is it?" Miss Cassie asks and I tell her.

She takes my hands and says, "Answer me this; what part of yourself keeps you safe?"

I know this. My positive "Controlling Me" is concerned with safety; I remember what Miss Tina taught us. I tell her.

"Good. So this is how you take charge of your negative 'Spontaneous Me.' Stand up straight and make your voice firm. Say, 'I am in control of this knife; this knife is not in control of me.'"

I try to stand as tall as I can. I clear my throat and I say deliberately, "I am in control of this knife; this knife is not in control of me."

"Say it again and really mean it," Miss Cassie says.

I grit my teeth and I'm determined to mean what I say. *"I am in control of this knife; this knife is not in control of me."*

"Go, girl," the girls say together, grinning at me.

"Now, pick up the knife and slice the cucumbers. You are in control of the knife; your 'Controlling Me' said so."

She pats my shoulder and says, "Good job" as she walks away. I feel better. I really *do* feel in control of myself. How can that happen when only a few minutes ago I was afraid? As I slice the cucumbers, it dawns on me why. I was scared because I was functioning from my "Spontaneous Me," but when I shifted to another part of myself, my "Controlling Me," I was able to beat my fear and feel in control of myself. How awesome is that? I smile to myself as I arrange the cucumbers neatly in a dish, and the knife lies nearby, powerless.

"Have you got anymore potatoes ready for the fire?"

I turn around and Franklin's standing next to me.

"Oh, wasn't that enough?" is all I can think of to say.

"Apparently not," Miss Cassie chips in. "Do some more, okay?"

I go over to the bag of baking potatoes and pick out as many as I can carry, but I drop several. Franklin bends down and picks them up. I feel stupid and my face burns. I wrap them clumsily in foil, hurrying as fast as I can, and when I hand them to him, my fingers touch his hand and I'm embarrassed. He looks at me but I look away. He leaves.

"Girl!" Leisha says, laughing. "They had enough potatoes. He came in here to see you. How obvious. Boys!"

I go back to rearranging the cucumbers in dishes, trying to ignore them all laughing. Miss Cassie shows me how to marinate the ribs, and I try to ignore the girls, but their jibes make me smile. I can't believe that a few minutes ago my thoughts were bogged down with the fear that I wouldn't be able to control my urge to cut, when all my thoughts now are focused around some goofy boy who's so obvious. I giggle along with the others as we chop vegetables and banter across the table.

An aide pokes her head around the door and says, "Marsha, you've got some visitors."

I look at Miss Cassie. She tells me to go. I follow her up the corridor and she shows me to a "Visitors Room." Anxiety flows through me... who's come to visit me?

The aide opens the door. Mom, Dad and Grandma look up at me as I stand in the doorway. My stomach churns with anxiety, and it's not my "anxiety habit."

This is real anxiety, and as I think it, I can't stop the thoughts that pop into my head; my anxiety is actually fear, and that's from my "Spontaneous Me." I'm being real.

Just then I hear a familiar voice. Miss Tina walks up behind me, and as I step into the room, she does, too. I'm so relieved.

"Hello. You must be Marsha's family. I'm Miss Tina."

She shakes their hands and takes a seat. She nods at me, telling me to sit next to her. She's between me and my family, and I'm glad.

"I know your name," Mom says looking confused, as if she's trying to remember something that's buried deep inside her head. "You're the one that told my daughter I shouldn't be so negative. You said that I was focusing upon negative thoughts instead of positive ones. You said that I was dwelling on my fears. You hurt me."

Mom's whining, and she's said the words "you said" twice. I remember the lists of words Miss Tina wrote to help us identify when someone was functioning from their "Modified Me" in a negative way. I wonder what Miss Tina will say to her.

She waits a moment before answering Mom; it's as if she's waiting for Mom to blow herself out. She speaks in a calm voice.

"It's true, you *can* spook yourself by being afraid of fear if you dwell on negative things. I'm sorry you felt hurt. That was not my intention. When I'm faced with awful situations, I try to stop myself from running with it. I try to think about it from every angle, including finding positive aspects about it, and that's what I wanted the kids to do. You have to have hope and faith."

"A fat lot of good hope and faith did me," Dad says bitterly.

Miss Tina says, "Sir, I'm so sorry that you lost your legs. I know it's going to be a huge adjustment for you, but this is what I mean about focusing on the negative and ignoring the positive. You're *alive*; you could have been killed. Try and focus upon the positive."

Mom grabs a tissue and sobs into it.

"You don't know what I've been through," she cries.

Grandma puts her arms around Mom, Dad looks away, and Miss Tina sits calmly in her chair. I'm embarrassed.

"I'm a little confused," Miss Tina says. "Ma'am, you haven't seen your daughter for days. She could have died, and yet you haven't even bothered to say 'Hello' to her. Everything you've said so far has been about you."

Mom looks stricken, and Grandma speaks for her.

"Don't speak to my daughter like that. Can't you see how upset she is? What kind of person are you, anyway?"

"I see many things, and the most glaringly obvious thing I see is that no one has asked Marsha how she's doing."

I cringe. I can't believe that Miss Tina has just spoken to my parents like that. If Dad had legs, I know he'd walk out. He just sits there, though, fuming.

"Why does everything have to be about Marsha?" Grandma asks. "She's selfish. How could she put everyone through this when she can see that we're all struggling?"

"What is it that you expect of her?" Miss Tina asks.

Dad says, "Well, she could have been more helpful. I was counting on her to hold things together while I was away."

"Sir," Miss Tina says deliberately, "she's a child. Your wife should have 'held things together,' not a child."

Mom cries harder and Grandma looks furious. Dad looks as if he doesn't know what to say, but then blurts out.

"My wife can't hold herself together, let alone the family."

Grandma shouts at him. "Don't you dare speak about my daughter like that. How dare you? Look at her, she's in pieces. You've always been unfeeling."

"Shut up, you old bag."

Miss Tina holds up her hand and raises her voice.

"Stop, that's enough. Ma'am," she turns to Grandma, "I'd like to speak to Marsha's parents alone, please."

I recognize that Miss Tina has just functioned from her "Controlling Me" in a positive way; she's just taken charge of the situation.

"What? No! My daughter needs me," Grandma says.

"Your daughter is a grown woman and does not *need* you to sit with her. Please, Ma'am, would you wait in the reception area?"

Mom looks horrified as Grandma stands and leaves the room, slamming the door. Tears flow down her face. Dad looks surprised but says nothing.

Miss Tina speaks out. "It seems to me that things have gotten a bit screwed up in your family. I sense that you have both expected Marsha to be the parent in your home, but she's just a child. You both need to be the parents, not her."

Dad finds his voice and snaps at Mom. "This is all your fault. You've never taken responsibility for anything. You've always been weak and dependent." He turns to Miss Tina with anguish on his face that turns my stomach, and says, "She's always been like this. I should have tried to make her grow up before, but I didn't know how. All the time I was around, I guess it didn't matter so much. When I went to Iraq,

I figured Marsha would hold things together."

"She's a child, sir," Miss Tina says gently.

Dad shakes his head, and says, "I know. I'm sorry, Marsha. I guess I was running away from everything."

Mom's still crying; she looks like a powerless child. "Why are you picking on me? I haven't done anything wrong."

Miss Tina still doesn't go over to comfort her, and I don't want to.

"No one's picking on you. We just have to be honest so that we can fix what's wrong in your family." Miss Tina turns to Dad. "Are you willing to work on it?"

He nods. She then asks Mom, who blows her nose and mumbles, "Yes."

"That's good," Miss Tina says. "What I'd like you to do is to take this literature home with you, read it, and then come back tomorrow, but without your mother because this is between you both. Then I'll help you to see what's going on, and how you can fix it."

Miss Tina stands up and opens the door. Mom's still crying but she wheels Dad out. Neither of them says "Goodbye" to me.

Miss Tina shuts the door.

"Okay, Marsha, tell me what you saw. What parts of themselves were your family functioning from?"

"Um, Mom was definitely coming from her negative 'Modified Me.' She was whining and being hysterical."

"Good job."

"Dad was coming from his 'Controlling Me' but in a negative way, because he was blaming Mom and making her feel bad."

"Excellent."

"Grandma was coming from her, um," I think for a moment. "That's hard. She could have been coming from her negative 'Controlling Me' when she said, 'Don't speak to my daughter like that.' But then when she said, 'Why does everything have to be about Marsha?' she sounded whiny, so she could have been coming from her negative 'Modified Me.'"

"Marsha, you are so smart," Miss Tina says, smiling at me.

"But she could also be coming from her negative 'Nurturing Me,' couldn't she?"

"Say why."

"Well, let me think. Didn't you say that someone using their 'Nurturing Me' in a negative way takes the power away from the other person? Well, I think that Grandma treats Mom as if she's a little kid."

"Well spotted," Miss Tina says. "I think so, too. She makes her powerless and encourages her to be helpless."

"But why?"

"Well, one reason could be so that your mom

continues to need her mom. Perhaps Grandma needs to be needed."

It dawns on me that Grandma only functions from the negative parts of herself, and I say so to Miss Tina.

"That's why I asked her to leave. Everything she said was negative. Your parents have to work out their problems on their own. I've given them the literature about the five parts of themselves, so when they come back tomorrow we'll work on what's really going on in your family."

I bite my lip, feeling anxious. How will Mom and Dad take it? I think they'll be mad.

Miss Tina gives me a hug and tells me it'll be all right. I smile bleakly at her. I've never seen anyone be strong around my mom and dad — well, apart from Evan — but that didn't do any good. I want Miss Tina to move in with us.

I go back to Miss Cassie's classroom. The girls are outside. I follow them to the beach.

"Hey, Marsha," Leisha calls. "Come and get some ribs."

"Yeah, c'mon," Miss Cassie says. "There's plenty, especially potatoes," and the girls crack up laughing.

Chapter Eight

The next morning in group, Miss Tina sits in her chair waiting for us to be quiet. All the kids are hyped up, talking about the barbecue. I notice Franklin smiling at me, and I smile back. He's goofy and shy.

"One of the things kids who cut themselves say is that they feel numb; they can't feel anything. Today we're going to look at why that should be."

We're quiet. I don't know why I feel numb.

"The answer lies in your 'Modified Me,'" Miss Tina says. "Remember, your 'Modified Me' is the part of you that adapts to your families so that you fit in. What if your parents grew up in families that forbid them from expressing any feelings?"

"Why would they do that?" Greg asks.

"Well, sometimes people can be really uncomfortable when others express their feelings, particularly if they're crying."

"Yeah, my dad's like that. He gets angry when Mom cries."

"Yeah, mine, too," a kid says.

"Kids raised in families where their parents are uncomfortable expressing their feelings learn, without being told, that they should hold their feelings in."

Some of the kids nod, saying that's how it is in their families.

I sit and think. My dad doesn't show his feelings at all, so is that why I can't? But that doesn't make sense because my mom does show her feelings all the time. I don't get it.

I tell Miss Tina what I'm thinking and she says, "You don't need both parents to show you that feelings are forbidden; just one will be enough. What does your dad think about your mom showing her feelings?" she asks.

"He hates it. He thinks she's hysterical and weak."

"Well, his disapproval of your mother would be enough to make sure that you hid your feelings."

"Oh. I can remember thinking that I never wanted to be like her after I heard him say bad things about her and my grandma."

"So you learned from your dad that there was something not right with showing feelings, and you didn't want him to say ugly things about you in the same way he did about your mom and grandma."

"I guess."

"Once you've learned to hide your feelings as a small child, it's like you have an 'anti-feeling-force-field' around you that won't let anything in or out. So even if you tell yourself to feel, it won't get through."

"So what can we do?" Candy asks, and other kids ask the same.

"We have to get through that 'anti-feeling-force-field.'"

Someone knocks on the door. A man pokes his head around the door.

"Hi, I'm Ken. I'm a counselor here. I've been away for a few days. Are you ready, Miss Tina?"

"Yes."

Ken closes the door and we look at each other, wondering what's going on. He comes back a minute later carrying a tiny baby.

"Ooooh," most of the girls cry. They jump up and so do I. The baby is gorgeous. It's asleep. Ken sits down and cradles it as we crowd around, even the boys.

Miss Tina laughs.

"Now we have the key."

"What d'you mean?" Macy asks.

Miss Tina walks over to the flipchart and draws a face. It has big eyes.

"Human beings are programmed to nurture creatures with big eyes and round, plump faces.

Babies have big eyes and plump faces. Human babies are totally helpless at birth, and if we weren't programmed to nurture, our babies would die and the human race could become extinct. Toy manufacturers exploit the fact that we're programmed this way. They make teddy bears and dolls with huge eyes because we're programmed to think they're cute, and so they'll sell more."

"How does that help us?" Greg asks.

"Babies are the key to tapping into your 'Nurturing Me,'" Miss Tina says.

"Okay, I get that, but how will that help us learn to feel?"

"Remember, you start to 'modify' the moment you're born. I want you to get in contact with yourself, the 'you' that you were before you started to adapt to your families, before you learned how to stifle your feelings. Marsha, come here."

She asks me to sit between her and Ken. He puts the baby in my arms. A tingle courses through me. It feels soft and warm, and smells like rose petals.

"I want you to imagine that Ken's new baby is you, as you were at a few days old."

My stomach churns and I get an urge to cry.

"She's beautiful, isn't she?" Miss Tina says, bobbing down in front of me. "*You're* beautiful, aren't you? Look how special you are; how perfect you are." She pauses for a moment and then asks me, "How can you take a knife to this beautiful child?"

I feel horrified and my head starts spinning so badly that I fear I may drop the baby. A sob escapes me, and I thrust the baby back onto Ken.

I'm shaking. The thought of someone cutting such a beautiful baby fills me with such horror that I want to throw up. It's unthinkable. I try to shake the image out of my head because I can't bear it.

"No," I cry. "No!"

Tears flow down my face and I don't know what's happening to me. My "anti-feeling-force-field" seems to be disintegrating, and I can't control the sobbing that escapes me as fleeting images of Shelley and Casey as newborn babies flash into my head. I love babies. How could anyone hurt them? The idea is just too awful to contemplate.

Miss Tina won't let me go back to my seat. She tells me to sit back down next to Ken. I don't want to; I want to run from the room. What's she going to do?

She bobs down again in front of me, and says, "Let me ask you again, Marsha, "How can you take a knife to this beautiful child?"

I'm trembling. "You can't," I whisper.

"No, you can't."

Miss Tina takes the baby from Ken again and my heart starts to race. I bristle when I realize that she's going to put the baby on my lap again.

"Take her," she demands. "She is you. Hold her tight so that she's safe."

Something powerful inside me overtakes my fear, and I feel compelled to take care of the baby. I ignore my body's trembling and I hold the baby firmly. She wakes but doesn't cry. She looks up at me and a tear rolls down my face again. She's beautiful. She coos and sneezes, and I giggle through my tears. Almost instantly she's asleep again, and I stroke her soft face.

Miss Tina smiles at me. "Aren't you beautiful? You could never hurt her, could you?"

"Never!" I say adamantly.

Miss Tina sits on the other side of me and talks to the rest of the kids who are watching. Some of the girls are sniffing. Franklin looks all gooey, but Greg looks a bit stressed.

"Okay, so what just happened here?" she asks.

No one answers. I certainly don't, because I have no idea, although I know that something big has just happened to me.

"Because you have an 'anti-feeling-force-field,' it's going to take something major to break through it, and that something is the one thing we humans are programmed to react to... babies. Seeing the baby automatically hooked into Marsha's positive 'Nurturing Me,' but suggesting that the baby was her as a newborn triggered a powerful nurturing reaction towards herself, her 'Spontaneous Me,' the part of her that has been buried under her 'Modified Me.' Marsha's 'Spontaneous Me' has been hidden away, too scared to come out of hiding, too hurt to show its face, but today she has glimpsed it. What we have to do now, so that Marsha doesn't lose sight of her true self, her 'Spontaneous Me,' the place where her true feelings live, is to do something to remind herself of how she was as a baby. This will constantly hook into her 'Nurturing Me' which will then keep her safe and stop her from cutting herself anymore."

"But what?" I ask shakily.

Miss Tina smiles as if she has a secret, and says, "Ah, that's for Miss Cassie to show you."

Ken takes the baby from me, and we're just about to get up and head off towards Miss Cassie's classroom, when Greg says, "But what happens if you can't stand babies?" He sounds upset.

We stand still and wait for Miss Tina to answer.

"Like I said, human beings are *programmed* to respond to babies, so if you have an adverse reaction to them, it's likely to be coming from your 'Modified Me.' You've *learned* to dislike them for some reason and that reason lies within your family."

He still looks upset.

Miss Tina says, "Whether you like babies or not, I still want you to go with the others and take part in this exercise, because going through it will likely break through your 'anti-feeling-force-field' when you're not expecting it to. Okay?"

"Okay," he shrugs.

"You *are* lucky," Leisha says. "*I* wanted to hold the baby."

I smile, and I swear the baby smell is still on me.

We bundle through Miss Cassie's classroom door in a noisy heap, and she tells us to settle down. We stand around the big table in the center of the room. The table is full of sewn fabric, the shape of which I can't make out, thin plastic ties, nail clippers, a heap of polyester filling, nail varnish, a bucket of sand, small plastic bags, combs, and three big boxes.

I'm intrigued. I don't know what she's going to say.

"Okay, listen up. Miss Tina has just shown you the key to breaking through your 'anti-feeling-force-field.' It's the pre-programmed drive to take care of babies. By suggesting that the baby represents you as you were before your 'Modified Me' began to develop, the 'Nurturing Me' reacts towards your buried 'Spontaneous Me.' Miss Tina said that although Marsha glimpsed that part of herself for the first time today, we have to find a way so that she doesn't lose sight of it. And this is what we're going to do."

She tips two of the boxes upside down and laughs when we look shocked. There are heads, arms and legs all over the table.

"You are each going to make a baby, one that will represent you before your 'Modified Me' started to develop, so that you won't lose sight of your 'Spontaneous Me.' In doing this, your 'Nurturing Me' will be constantly connected to your 'Spontaneous Me.' Your 'Nurturing Me' will allow you to *feel* but will keep you safe when you feel."

Miss Cassie looks at me, and I shiver when she asks, "Can you take a knife to yourself as a baby? Can you?"

"Never."

"Good, and that's the whole point of this exercise. Once you get in touch with yourself as you were before all your feelings were stifled and hidden, there's absolutely no way that you could *ever* hurt yourself again. It's unthinkable. Okay," she says happily, "let's start."

I don't know what to do, but she tells us all to sit down and starts to show us how to remake ourselves. It's fascinating. She takes one of the sewn shapes, which turns out to be a body, and slips two feet into the legs and secures them with a thin plastic tie. Then she does the same with the plastic hands, and attaches them to the arms. She stuffs the body, arms and legs with polyester filling, puts a bag of sand inside the head and then attaches it to the body.

"Wow, that's amazing," Candy says.

"Hang on," Miss Cassie says, obviously enjoying herself. "I'm not finished yet."

She empties out the third box and there's a pile

of tiny baby clothes. She dresses the baby in an all-in-one suit and then puts the baby on her shoulder and pats its back as if trying to make it burp. We laugh. It's spooky because it looks so real.

"Right, now it's your turn. You are going to re-make you. I want you to sort through the heads to find one that has the same color hair and eyes as you have, and then make your baby-self just like I've shown you. Take your time and enjoy it."

I've got dark hair and dark eyes, so I sort through all the heads on the table until I find one that matches my complexion. She's got a cute smile. I pick out the other things I need and go towards a separate table to make my baby-self. The body reminds me of a skinny chicken, and it makes me giggle. It looks even funnier after I've attached the hands and feet, but as I stuff the body with filler, it starts to take on its own form. I feel excitement course through me, as my key to breaking down my "anti-feeling-force-field" is nearly finished.

"When you've finished, come and find the outfit you want for your baby-self. Choose it carefully because it's for you and you have to be happy with it."

I put the bag of sand inside the head and, as I attach it to the body, the head flops back exactly the same as Ken's new baby did when Miss Tina put her in my arms.

I leave my baby-self on the table and go to hunt

for an outfit. I choose a pink and white suit and a cute, matching pink-hooded jacket. There's a smile on my face; I can't help it. I wish Shelley were here; she'd love to do this. I take care dressing my baby-self, and when I'm satisfied, I pick her up and find myself hugging her. She's beautiful. Her hands and feet are weighted so she flops just like a new-born baby. My heart swells and I love her instantly. What's happening to me? If Tessa could see me now, she'd think I'd lost my mind, but I don't care. I feel good.

I sit down and watch the others in various stages of remaking their baby-selves. They make me laugh. Greg is gritting his teeth, stuffing filling into his body. "How come one leg is fatter than the other," he complains. "Oh, this is too hard." Macy and Poppy have finished their babies and are arguing over the same outfit. Leisha has finished hers and is sitting there, lost in her own little world, humming to the baby slung over her shoulder. She's so cool. I love her. She doesn't care what anyone thinks about her. Candy's tongue is sticking out with concentration as she tries to attach the head to the body, but her hands slip, and she cusses when the head rolls along the table and falls to the floor. I giggle because it seems so bizarre.

Miss Tina walks into the classroom.

"Oh, my," she says, "look at all these wonderful baby-selves." She takes my baby and holds her.

"Oh, she's beautiful, just like you." She gives my baby-self back to me and walks around looking at what the others have made.

Franklin comes over to me. "Will you help me?" he asks. "Something's wrong with my head."

I snort with laughter. He looks goofy and grins. "Okay, okay, I know there's always been something wrong with my head."

"You haven't put the bag of sand in it."

"Oh, yeah." He walks off with his chicken-like body jammed under his armpit, and his head in his hand, searching for a bag of sand. When he comes back, he's grinning.

"Okay, now help me get my head on straight. I don't want my face looking backwards."

I put my baby-self down on the table and feel strange. It looks so weird... a baby left on a table. I hold his body while he threads the tie through the neck and then positions the head where he wants it.

"If the kids at school could see me now, they'd think I'd lost my marbles," he says. But then he grins at me. "It's kind of fun though, isn't it?"

"Yeah." I pick up my baby-self from the table and feel a strange sense of calm come over me. This is too weird.

"Come and help me choose an outfit. You're a girl; you know these things."

Miss Tina hears him and says, "Franklin," in a stern voice that I know has just come from her positive "Controlling Me." He gets up and looks at me, saying, "Forget it, I'll choose for myself."

Miss Tina smiles at us and I get the feeling that she's really enjoying herself. Miss Cassie wanders around helping kids anchor their heads onto their bodies, saying "Good job," when their baby-selves take shape.

One by one we finish and Miss Tina stands in front of us. Miss Cassie sits down to listen.

"You've all done so well. I hope you've enjoyed yourselves. It's not often that you get to remake yourself. Okay, this 'baby' represents your 'Spontaneous Me,' the part of you that feels, but the part of you that's been hidden because you aren't allowed to *feel* in your families. It is the key that will establish a connection between your 'Nurturing Me' and your 'Spontaneous Me,' which when strengthened will enable you to feel all your feelings safely. It will enable you to use your 'Nurturing Me' to be able to take care of you forevermore so that you will never *ever* hurt yourself again."

She looks around the classroom, and I sense that she moves from functioning from her "Thinking Me" to her positive "Controlling Me" when she says, "Pick up your baby-selves." She waits while we do as she asks. "Your 'baby' is you before you learned to stifle your feelings. It has your name. You may call your baby-self by your actual name or a nickname version of it, but nothing else, for your 'baby' is *you*."

Everyone talks at once, trying to decide what to call their baby-selves. My name's Marsha. I've never had a nickname, or a baby name. It feels weird to call my doll "Marsha," and I don't know what else to do. Franklin says his mom used to call him "Frankie," so that's what he's going to call his baby-self. I look at my doll and suddenly I'm reminded of Casey, who has the same dark hair and dark eyes as me. When he was little he couldn't say, "Marsha." He used to say, "Shar-sha." That's what I'm going to name my baby-self... Sharsha.

Miss Tina waits until we stop talking and says, "You don't need to tell anyone what your baby-self is called. This is a relationship between you and your baby-self and no one else, okay? It's private."

I'm glad.

"From now on you will carry your baby-self around with you wherever you go. You will do this so that your 'Nurturing Me' gets used to taking care of the vulnerable side of yourselves, the part where your feelings are. You will express your feelings, knowing that you are totally safe because your 'Nurturing Me' is watching out for you. You'll never feel alone again, and you'll never hurt yourself again. Could you take a knife to this beautiful child?" she asks deliberately.

The classroom is quiet. No one says anything at first. How could anyone cut a child with a knife? That's what my "Spontaneous Me" is, the child in me.

"No!" I say definitely.

"Me neither."

"Nor me."

"Or me."

All the kids say the same. Miss Tina smiles and shakes her head at the same time. "You're all so awesome. So strengthen your 'Nurturing Me's' and make sure you take care of yourselves so that you never cut yourselves again. Let your feelings out, knowing that your 'Nurturing Me' will protect and care for you. Be who you really are, and feel."

Miss Cassie stands up and walks around the classroom handing out what looks like a scarf.

Miss Tina says, "Miss Cassie is handing out a sling. You'll carry your baby-self around with you until the day you leave here. It will serve as a reminder that your 'Nurturing Me' is working to protect your 'Spontaneous Me' so that you can express your feelings safely."

Miss Cassie gets to me and hands out a pale pink triangle scarf. When we each have one, she stands behind me and ties it so that Sharsha is held firmly in front of me. She's not in my way at all, and as I get used to the knot in the scarf pressing against my shoulder blade, I feel a strange sense of comfort knowing she's there.

Miss Tina and Miss Cassie go around tying our baby-selves to us, and I stand there watching. It feels weird; this would never happen at school. The kids wouldn't understand; they'd laugh or perhaps they'd be scared, but here, in this safe place, it feels right. We're all the same. We each cut ourselves because we can't feel, and because we don't have access to our "Spontaneous Me" and our "Nurturing Me." I'm glad I'm not at school. I want to be here at Beach Haven where I can be the real me. I don't know who that is yet, but I'm looking forward to meeting the real Marsha, the real Sharsha. And as I think it, my arms automatically fold around my baby-self tied against me.

I have no explanation for it, but a strange sense of calm comes over me.

Macy looks at Miss Tina quizzically and asks, "How did you think of such a thing?"

Miss Tina tells us all to sit down. Sharsha nestles into me and instinctively I rest my arms around her. I look around and see that everyone's doing the same, even Greg. It would be hard to ignore a baby resting in your lap, or to let your arms hang down to the sides. It feels natural to cradle her. I can't stop the nurturing feelings that flow through me, and it dawns on me that this is what Miss Tina wants to happen.

"I was inspired by the English author, Philip Pullman. He wrote a trilogy for children, well, adults too, called *The Golden Compass, The Subtle Knife and The Amber Spyglass*. I won't tell you the plot or I'll ruin the surprise; they're in our library if you want to read them.

"In one of the worlds he described, everyone's soul lived outside their body in the form of an animal. The little girl in the story, Lyra, loved and revered her soul and would never do anything to hurt it. Her soul was like a constant companion. The image this made in my mind moved me so much, because it dawned on me that if we could see our souls, or our true selves, it would be absolutely impossible to hurt them.

"When I thought about kids cutting themselves, divorced from their real selves because they'd learned to stifle all their feelings, I wondered if they would cut if their soul lived outside of their bodies. Leisha, if you were like Lyra in Philip Pullman's books and your soul was a little fluffy puppy dog, could you slice it with a knife, like you've done to your arms?"

Leisha shudders and looks shaken.

"No! That's horrible. I could never."

"Listen to yourself," Miss Tina says. "Why is it so unthinkable when that's exactly what you do to yourself?"

"But your soul is something precious," Leisha says.

"Sweet girl, you *are* your soul, and *you are* precious."

We fall silent and Miss Tina continues.

"Our souls don't live outside our bodies like in

the world Lyra comes from, but I sat and thought about Philip Pullman's idea and how we'd feel if the tiny child we started out as in *this* world lived outside ourselves to remind us how precious we are. The more I thought about it, I knew that if we could see our true selves, our 'Spontaneous Me,' as precious and vulnerable, then it would be impossible to cut ever again."

"I never will again," I say, and several others say the same.

"When you understand the five parts of yourself, it's easy to see why Lyra's soul was in the form of an animal; an animal elicited love from her. The soul was the 'Spontaneous Me' watched over and cared for by her 'Nurturing Me.' It's the same thing when you see your baby-self. Your baby-self represents your 'Spontaneous Me' before you learned to modify yourself to fit into your families. It connects powerfully to your 'Nurturing Me,' which will watch over you and care for you.

"Once you can see yourself in this way, it will be impossible for you to cut yourself ever again. You will love yourself, and when you feel hurt or are in pain, you'll be able to soothe yourself from your 'Nurturing Me.'" She smiles, and says, "Trust me, it's true."

Chapter Nine

There's a knock on the door. The receptionist pokes her head in.

"Visitors for Marsha."

Miss Tina looks at me.

"That'll be your parents. They're here for a family session. Are you ready?"

I go to remove the doll tied to my chest and Miss Tina says, "Oh, no. Your baby-self stays with you all the time."

I'm scared. What will Mom and Dad say? I can just picture it. Dad will be scathing and will laugh at me, and Mom will think I'm a hopeless case and will be hysterical. I can't do anything about it, though, because Miss Tina has said that all us kids have to take our baby-selves everywhere with us. I have no choice.

I head towards the "Visitors Room" with Miss Tina walking alongside me. "It'll be all right. Don't you worry."

I wait for her to go into the room first. I creep in behind her. I wait for Mom or Dad to say something about the doll lodged in the sling around my body, but they don't say anything. I'm amazed. I can't believe it. I sit down and, as Miss Tina talks, I forget about my baby-self being here in the room.

"Did you read the literature I gave you?"

"Yes, we did. It was very interesting," Dad says. Mom doesn't say anything.

"What did you think about it?"

"Well, I saw myself in it quite a bit."

"You did? Which bit?"

Dad coughs and looks uncomfortable. "It's obvious that I use the 'Controlling Me' part of myself a lot."

Miss Tina beams at him.

"Sir, I'm so proud of you. You're right. What did you think about it?" she asks Mom.

Mom sniffs. "I didn't understand it. My mother told me it's a load of rubbish."

"That's interesting," Miss Tina says, "I wonder why. Y'know, it doesn't matter if you don't understand something, what matters is that you open your mind to something new. I gave you the means to be able to understand yourselves and your behavior. Let's look at it now."

Dad looks willing but Mom shifts in her chair and looks uncomfortable.

There's a flipchart in the room and Miss Tina starts to draw the picture of our personalities. I feel anxious and it's not my 'anxiety habit,' it's real fear. I draw my arms tighter around Sharsha and instantly I feel comforted.

Beneath the picture of our personalities, Miss Tina draws the bar chart and explains that to be emotionally healthy, everyone should have equal amounts of energy available in each of the five parts of our personalities for the appropriate situation. She turns the page and draws two smaller diagrams of ourselves and writes "Mom" and "Dad" above them.

"As children, we learn how to fit into our families... you know that from the literature I gave you. Sometimes children learn to be helpless, to be sick, to be demanding, or to please — the list is endless — all in order to get their needs met. A small child has no power around adults, and if his needs aren't met, if parents are too busy or are too preoccupied with themselves, the child has no choice but to adapt his behaviour so that his needs *will* be met. That's how the 'Modified Me' develops, and it's different for every child because families differ. Are you with me?"

"Yes," Dad says. Mom sniffs.

"Only you know how you had to adapt to your family. I wasn't there, so I can't tell you for certain how you had to modify yourself, but I can make an educated guess by the way you behave now."

I don't know if it's my imagination, but Sharsha seems to feel warm in my arms. I hold her close and I'm amazed; I feel safe.

"Sir, I suspect that in your family, feelings were banned. They were seen as being weak."

Dad looks at her, and something about his face makes my stomach churn. He looks in pain.

"You're absolutely right," he falters.

"And Mom, I suspect that in your family, you were allowed to show your feelings."

Mom nods.

"I also suspect that it was a bit of a competition to see who could feel the most."

Mom nods again, and I feel that she's finally listening because she doesn't sniff.

"Okay, let's look at what's happened to your personalities, how you've adapted and modified them to fit in with your families. There's no blame, you know, only understanding. Once you understand why you behave the way you do, you can change things."

Miss Tina points to the picture of Mom and Dad. She takes a different colored marker and starts to draw lines around different parts of themselves. I don't know what she's going to say next and I listen intently.

"This is how I see it," she says. "I see that Mom uses only her 'Modified Me' and her 'Spontaneous

Me,' and has learned in her family that someone else will come to her rescue, think for her and tell her what to do. All things that her 'Thinking Me' and her 'Controlling Me' should be doing."

Mom gasps.

"Now Dad, you come from a family where feelings are forbidden, so you are not using your 'Spontaneous Me,' but you make up for Mom's lack of thinking skills and self control. You inadvertently *enable* your wife to be helpless and dependent by thinking for her and taking charge of everything."

Miss Tina draws one continuous loop around parts of the two diagrams, and says, "You are acting as one individual when you are really two, with all five parts of your personalities available to you, if you'd only use them. You are ignoring parts of yourselves so that you blend into each other and function as one person. That's called 'co-dependence.'"

I look at what she's drawn and it makes sense.

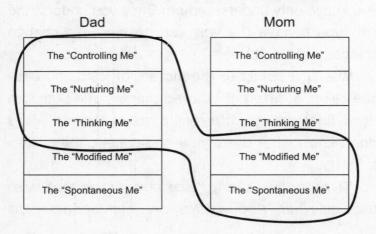

Dad	Mom
The "Controlling Me"	The "Controlling Me"
The "Nurturing Me"	The "Nurturing Me"
The "Thinking Me"	The "Thinking Me"
The "Modified Me"	The "Modified Me"
The "Spontaneous Me"	The "Spontaneous Me"

Mom looks as if she's about to cry, and I understand. Miss Tina *is* very honest and sometimes it's hard to hear what she says.

"This picture represents a couple who are codependent. Mom, what you need to do is... you need to think for yourself and stop letting people rescue you, especially your child. Marsha is just a child; she shouldn't be your parent. You are *her* parent."

Mom is speechless.

"Dad, stop rescuing your wife. Let her think for herself and take responsibility for her behavior. Let her take control of herself. What *you* need to do is to access your 'Spontaneous Me.' Learn to have fun, hang loose, and chill out. Just don't rescue your wife, okay?"

"Okay," Dad says quickly. "I see what you're getting at."

He glances at Mom and there's something on his face that I can't fathom. He looks sad, I think.

"It looks as if you are functioning mainly from your negative 'Controlling Me,'" Miss Tina says to my dad. "And the reason I say it's negative is because you're not only concerned with safety, which would be this part of yourself used positively, but you seem irritated with everyone around you. Does that fit?"

Dad looks crestfallen. "Yes, I guess it does. I don't mean to be picky, I just get frustrated. Sometimes I feel as if I'm running this family on my own, so I get grumpy."

"Using your 'Controlling Me' in a negative way is very damaging to those who are subjected to it," Miss Tina says without recrimination. "Were your parents like that?"

"Not my mother, no, but my father was. He continually picked fault with me and told me I was no good. I wanted to be like him. He loved the military and always wanted me to join. I wanted him to be proud of me." Dad's voice changes, he sounds choked. "But I failed. They wouldn't let me join. I was never good enough, but when they needed soldiers for the Iraq war, they let me in."

He swallows hard and I feel sick. I hold Sharsha tight against me. He tries to talk but breaks down. "I feel so betrayed."

"By whom?" Miss Tina asks.

"My dad. He led me to believe that going to war was exciting, but it's hell, sheer hell. I wish I'd never seen the things I've seen." He clears his throat as if there's something in it that's going to choke him. "I wish I'd never gone. I'd still have my legs."

Miss Tina sits down and looks at both of them while I hug my baby-self, feeling protected by her. As I think it, I try to work out why I feel the way I do. I can't be protected by a baby doll, that's stupid. I know I can't be protected by my "Spontaneous Me" either, it doesn't work that way. Then it dawns on me... I feel protected with Sharsha in my arms because I've activated my "Nurturing Me." Awesome! I smile to myself, but it quickly disappears.

Dad cries and I feel terrible. I don't know what to do. Mom starts crying, too. She's no help to Dad; Miss Tina sits and watches. I want to go over to Dad to comfort him, but I sit still not knowing what to do. When he stops crying, he looks up and wipes his eyes and nose on the back of his sleeve. Miss Tina hands him a box of tissues.

Mom ventures to speak out. "I hated your dad. He was so judgmental. I know he hated me. Don't pretend that he didn't."

Dad doesn't say anything. He can't even manage a shrug.

"He made me feel stupid and inadequate all the time," Mom says.

Miss Tina seems to be able to steer them away from recriminations and asks, "How did you both meet?"

Mom and Dad's faces brighten. I can't believe that my mom is the same person as she recounts how she and Dad met. She's nothing like the abusive, hateful person she is at home. Something weird settled over me... perhaps I don't know my mom at all. I hold Sharsha close to me and gain comfort from her.

Mom's eyes twinkle. "He was my hero, and I was his princess. He was so stiff, so upright and proper; so different from me," she giggles. "I think I confused him. He called me his 'little butterfly' because I would flit about. Sometimes he'd scratch his head when I slid down the slide on a playground, as if he couldn't figure me out. But he seemed to want what I had, and I forced him to climb to the top of the slide and slip down after me. He'd laughed and said that he'd never had so much fun."

I know this story; it's the one Mom used to tell me all the time when I was little.

"You should have seen me in my wedding dress; I was like a fairy princess, but Dad stood there, stiff, rigid and proper."

I remember seeing Mom and Dad's wedding photos. Dad stood rigidly while Mom clung onto his arm with her leg bent up behind her, pulling a goofy face. The family photo showed Dad's parents standing there as rigid as he was, and Mom's parents laughing, dressed in wild clothes. I suddenly understand what Miss Tina is talking about. Dad has learned from his family to be austere and unfeeling, while Mom has learned to live off her feelings. Neither way is right.

I venture to speak. "How come you found each other attractive? After all, you were so different. How come you chose each other?"

"It's no mystery, although it may seem as if it is," Miss Tina says before they can answer. "People choose each other subconsciously, that means without conscious thought. They identify those who'll play the same kind of *games* they're used to playing in their families. It's what they feel *at home* with. Your mom was subconsciously searching for a man who would take charge and who wasn't emotional. She couldn't cope with someone who was equally as emotional as her, because she couldn't be sure that he would take care of her.

"You dad was subconsciously searching for someone who could teach him how to play, but when he was faced with it every day, his austere, persecutory negative 'Controlling Me,' a replica from his own father, kicked in. He couldn't cope with your mother's playfulness or her display of feelings. The more he criticized, the more helpless she felt. Am I right?" Miss Tina asks Mom.

She nods miserably.

"And so you both became locked into exactly the same way your parents behaved, right?"

They both say, "Yes."

Miss Tina suddenly sounds cheerful. "But that's okay, because now that you know all this, you can change, can't you? Own all five parts of your personalities and function as two separate individuals. Be parents to your children and don't expect them to parent you."

Mom and Dad nod and say they will. Miss Tina stands up to leave and I get up, too. I don't want to be alone in the room with them.

Mom mumbles, "I'm sorry I dumped on you so

much, Marsha. I'll try to do better, I promise."

Dad looks like he really hurts inside. "I'm so sorry that I blamed you for the loss of my legs. Of course it wasn't your fault. I was in the wrong place at the wrong time, that's all."

I glance at Mom, expecting her to protest as he echoes Miss Tina's words, but she just shrugs. I hug Dad and tell him that I really am glad he's home. Mom stands there looking awkward. I don't want to hug her but she looks so forlorn that I do it anyway.

Sharsha gets in the way and Mom says, "What *is* that inside there?"

I don't show her, but I say, "Myself."

She looks confused and just says, "Oh."

As they leave Miss Tina says, "A word of advice — ask your mother to go home."

Dad grins and says, "Will do," as Mom wheels him up the corridor.

"That went rather well," Miss Tina says, grinning at me.

I have an overwhelming urge to giggle. I can't believe Miss Tina laid it out so blatantly for them to see. It was awesome.

"Very well," I say.

"How did you feel sitting there with your baby-self?"

"Awkward at first, but having her there made me feel safe."

"Do you understand why?"

"Yes, because she hooks into my 'Nurturing Me,' and that part of me keeps me safe."

Miss Tina pats me on the back and tells me that I'm too smart.

I find the others outside on the beach. I giggle to myself as I stumble over the loose sand. They all look like pregnant aliens, with their baby-selves protruding out in front of them. Sharsha isn't heavy, nor is she in my way.

I slump down on the sand next to the girls.

"How did your family session go?" Candy asks.

"It was pretty good, actually. I'm surprised because I thought Mom and Dad would go nuts having someone tell them what they should be doing, but they seemed to listen. Miss Tina was awesome, she let them have it with both barrels."

"Yes, she can be like that," Macy says. "She did the same with my parents."

"Did they listen?" I ask.

"Yeah, they did. They got really into it and started telling each other which part of themselves they were coming from. It was like they had a new toy to play with at Christmas... 'Spot the personality part.' It was funny. They said that they'd never view life in the same way again, and said that going out to eat and people-watching was more fun than going to the movies."

I laugh. I know what she means. I hope my mom

and dad really get into it, too.

Leisha slips her baby-self out of her sling. She cradles her. "Isn't it a weird feeling?" she says, playing with her baby's hair, which is the same dark shade as her own. "I played with dolls when I was little, but this feels different."

"I don't think we're expected to play with them," Franklin says, flopping down on the sand next to me.

"I know that," she says, rolling her eyes at him.

I think to myself that she's just slipped into her negative "Modified Me" but she quickly reverts back into her "Thinking Me."

"I've never felt protective towards myself before, but if I look at this doll and tell myself that she represents me as a newborn baby, I feel fiercely protective. It's really weird. I won't let anyone hurt her... me. Miss Tina's right, it *is* unthinkable to cut myself again."

"I know just what you mean," I say. "When I was in my family session, I was scared. I didn't know whether my parents were going to pick on me or not, but something inside me changed as I felt my baby-self next to me. I felt protective, too, and it chased my fear away. Okay, having Miss Tina sort my folks out helped," I grin remembering her stern tone of voice as she told them how it was, "but I felt calm and determined inside. I wasn't going to let anyone hurt me."

Franklin asks, "So were you coming from your 'Controlling Me' or your 'Nurturing Me' then?"

"Oh ho, smart question," Macy says, smiling.

I think for a moment. "Both, I guess. I was keeping myself safe, which comes from my 'Controlling Me' and yet I was also taking care of me, which comes from my 'Nurturing Me.' Yeah, both."

"Cool," Franklin says.

He gets his baby-self out, too. Seeing a guy holding a doll that looks so much like a real baby makes me go all gooey. There's something wonderful about a guy with a baby. Well, that's what I think anyway.

Greg joins us.

"Me, myself and I are hot. Well, in this case, me and my baby-self are hot."

He tries to fan his doll, but it's strapped to him. He looks silly and I laugh along with the others. He pulls the doll out of the sling and lays it across his knees.

The seagulls are screeching overhead, and suddenly something lands on Greg's baby-self. The seagull has pooped.

Greg looks indignant. "Hey," he shouts, when he sees a wad on his baby-self's outfit.

We laugh.

"I guess my baby has pooped and needs a diaper change," he quips. Then he holds his baby-self up and says, "D'you think he looks like me?"

"Well, now that you mention it, he does," Poppy says, getting her baby-self out, too.

Soon we're all holding our baby-selves and I smile as a silly thought pops into my head. If someone walked along the beach and looked at us sitting around in a group holding tiny babies, they would think they'd stumbled upon a home for unmarried parents and their babies. I smile to myself, and as the thought settles in my mind, I giggle.

"What're you laughing about?" Candy asks.

I tell her and she laughs, too.

Greg says, "C'mon, let's walk along the beach. Don't put the dolls in their slings. C'mon, it'll be fun."

Leisha jumps up and I cringe, but laugh, as she almost drops her baby-self and grabs it by the ankle.

"Oops," she says, biting her lip. "Sorry," she whispers into her baby-self's ear. She strokes its hair down and grins at me.

I jump up, too, and so do the others one by one. We hold our baby-selves in our arms and walk along the shore, dodging the waves that roll up the sand. I can't help myself; I've got the giggles badly. I know what a weird bunch we must look like.

As we come towards people who are sun bathing or wading in the surf, we cradle our "babies" and croon at them. They do a double-take, like they can't quite believe what they're seeing, but no one approaches us. They just whisper among themselves.

When we get to the other end of the cove, Greg, who's enjoying himself, says, "Right, now let's give them a show. Are you ready? I bet I can beat you back to Beach Haven."

I snort with laughter as he shoots off, his "baby" locked in one arm and the other flailing about as he tries to keep his balance in the loose sand. He looks so funny. The others charge after him, and I'm laughing so hard that I wet myself.

I have no choice but to follow them. So I lock my left arm around Sharsha and run across the sand after the others, slipping everywhere. I'm aware that everyone on the beach stops what they're doing to watch us.

I can barely breathe by the time I get back to the beach in front of Beach Haven. I flop down on the sand and laugh like I've never laughed before.

"Did you see their faces?" Greg asks, laughing so hard he can hardly get his words out.

No one can answer him because we're laughing so much. I catch my breath, and as my breathing slows a weird feeling comes over me. If Sharsha were real, would I have charged up the shore with her bouncing about in my arms? The answer is "No," and suddenly I feel weird. I have an overwhelming urge to hold her tight and to make her safe.

The bell rings telling us that it's dinner time. We

slip our baby-selves back into their slings and head inside.

After dinner we go to group. Miss Tina's already waiting for us.

"Tonight we're going to talk about becoming addicted to cutting and what to do about it. What does 'being addicted' mean?"

Macy says, "When you've got to have something."

"When you feel as if you'll go crazy if you don't get whatever you're addicted to," Greg says.

"When you have no control over yourself to stop it," Candy adds.

"When you need whatever it is to make you feel better, or to help you cope with something," I say, thinking about Mom drinking alcohol.

Miss Tina scribbles down our answers on the flip-chart as we call out.

"People can be addicted to all kinds of things: smoking, overeating, gambling, lying, drugs, alcohol, irresponsible sex, TV and video games, spending money, chocolate, and of course, cutting. All these things take the person away from their pain for a short while, and that's why, and how, people become addicted to things. Being addicted to drugs and smoking is harder to beat because the body becomes physically dependent on the substance and craves it in order to feel 'normal,' but being addicted to the other things can be thought of as a bad habit. And bad habits can be changed."

"Not easily, though," Franklin says.

Miss Tina nods. "That's true, but they *can* be changed nevertheless. Let's look at some ways of changing bad habits, and in particular the 'cutting' bad habit."

She turns to a fresh page and starts to write.

Self-talk
Goal setting
Dealing with stress
Deep breathing
Relaxation
Visualization
Alternative behaviors

She sits down.

"Self-talk means what it says. You talk to yourself."

"Won't people think we're crazy?" Greg quips.

"Not if you do it when you're alone," Miss Tina answers him. "Now that you know about the five parts of your personality, when you talk to yourself you can come from any one of those five parts. What do you think each part would say?"

She steps over to the flipchart again.

"What would your 'Controlling Me' say?"

"Don't cut yourself. Find another way to get your feelings out," Leisha says.

"And your 'Nurturing Me'?"

"Let your feelings out safely. I'm here for you," Macy says.

"Good," Miss Tina comments. "I like that. And your 'Thinking Me'?"

"If I cut myself I'll never get better. Let me think of other ways to get rid of my stress, pain, feelings... whatever," Poppy says.

"Excellent. What about from your "Modified Me'?"

We become quiet. I don't know.

Greg speaks out. "I'm going to cut anyway. It's my body. I'll force everyone to give me some attention."

"Ouch," Macy says.

Miss Tina smiles at Greg. "Can you hear how stubborn Greg sounded? He sounded like he was refusing to try to give up his bad habit, like he's going to keep on doing it to spite other people. What would your 'Spontaneous Me' say?"

"Don't hurt me," I say.

Miss Tina puts the pen down and looks at what she's written.

"Okay, so you can talk to yourself from four of the five parts of your personality to help you stop cutting. We want to silence your negative 'Modified Me,' right?"

"Right," we reply.

"You can set goals for yourself, too. That would

help. Try setting little goals first that you know you can keep, like, 'I won't cut for an hour,' and then gradually increase the time.

"One of the biggest reasons that people slip back into bad habits, or give in to their addictions, is stress. If they can't cope with stress, they turn to something to help them cope. When you're stressed, adrenaline flies around your body and makes you sweat, your heart races, and it makes you panic. What you have to do is to learn to relax. You can do this with deep breathing exercises. Count to five as you breathe in, hold your breath for five seconds and then count to five as you exhale.

"You can put your headphones on and listen to music — soothing music, not aggressive rock. You can take a warm bubble bath. You can lie still and visualize yourself in a beautiful place next to a stream; the sound of water is so relaxing. Practice these things and they'll help you relax, and then the urge to cut will pass."

I feel sleepy just listening to her.

"Another thing you can do is to replace the behavior with another, safer behavior. When you cut, your body experiences sensations. Replace that sensation with another."

She walks around the room and hands us each a bottle of lotion.

"Each time you get the urge to cut, massage your arms with this lotion. Your body will experience sensations, but you'll be distracting yourself from the urge to cut by doing an alternative behavior. When the urge passes, which it will, your body will feel soothed, and the lotion will help reduce your angry scars. If you do this, you'll automatically tap into your 'Nurturing Me' which will take care of you. And you'll smell nice too," she adds, smiling at us.

Chapter Ten

Miss Tina tells us to keep the bottle of lotion with us at all times so that if the urge to cut should sneak up on us, we'll be prepared. Then she lets us go for the evening.

I follow the others into the living room and sink into a squashy sofa while the kids argue over what channel to put on the TV. They settle for a game show. I can't be bothered to watch it, so I go outside and sit on a swing and watch the waves roll up the beach. I hear someone behind me and glance over my shoulder. It's Franklin.

"D'you want some company?" he asks.

"Okay."

He sits on the swing next to me and we sway idly.

"It's been a hectic day, hasn't it? We covered a lot," he says, shifting his baby-self to get it comfortable.

"Yeah, definitely. It's been a good day, though. I feel different from how I felt this time yesterday."

"In what way?"

"Well..." I think about how to answer. "I'm not really sure. I guess it must be having to face my baby-self all the time. Of course I'm aware of it being tied to me, although it's not in my way, but it's more than that. It's presence, or rather I should say, '*her* presence,' really does tap into my 'Nurturing Me,' and for the first time in my life I feel nurturing towards myself. I didn't feel like this yesterday, so that's what the difference must be."

"I know what you mean," he says without saying any more.

We're silent for a moment as I think.

"Listen, I don't want to be sexist or anything, but people expect girls to be into babies, so is that why this is having such a weird effect on me? What I want to know is, if boys aren't so into babies, will it have the same effect on them?" I ask.

"I don't know," he answers honestly. "I've got younger brothers and Mom made me help a lot when they were little, so I'm used to babies and I like them. I don't know how I'd feel if I didn't like them. I guess you should ask Greg how he feels."

"So how do *you* feel? Is carrying around your baby-self having a weird effect on you?"

"Yes," he confesses. "I've never cared about myself before either, but I can't ignore myself if

I'm tiny and vulnerable. It hooks into my 'Nurturing Me,' too. It feels very strange. I know we had a laugh racing on the beach today," he grins, "but seriously I feel really protective towards myself, and when I look at him, he makes me smile."

He fumbles inside his sling and out pokes this cute, cheeky face with blonde hair and blue eyes.

The sight of him makes me go gooey. He's so cute. I reach inside my sling and make Sharsha's head poke out, too.

Franklin says, "Ahhh, she's so cute." Then he makes his baby-self wave and I make Sharsha wave back, and we giggle. It's funny.

"I told you what my baby-self is called. What's yours called?"

I don't mind telling him. I explain about Casey not being able to say my name when he was little.

"Sharsha," he says slowly. "That's pretty."

"Thank you."

We fall silent until I blurt out. "What's it like for a guy to cut?"

"Why d'you ask?"

"Well, I just imagined that it would be different, that's all."

He shakes his head. "I don't think there's any difference. I cut when I can't stand the pressure and the pain inside me anymore. Isn't that the reason why you cut?"

"Yes. I'm sorry. I just thought it might be different," I say, feeling stupid.

"Well, I guess there is one difference."

"What?"

"It's easier for guys to hide it because we can always wear long sleeves, whereas girls, especially in the summer, wear short sleeves or sleeveless tops."

I nod my head slowly, thinking. "Yeah, I can see that."

"I admire Macy and Candy for wearing short sleeves," I say. "I don't think I'll ever be able to wear short sleeves again."

"Are your arms a mess then?"

I feel ashamed and automatically pull Sharsha nearer to me for comfort. I nod.

"Mine, too," he says, pulling his sleeves up.

His arms are covered in angry, red criss-crosses. Not one area is free of them. I swallow hard. I unhook my thumbs from my cuffs slowly and roll my sleeves up, exposing the same hideous patterns. I roll them back down quickly to hide my shame, and slip my thumbs into their place.

We fall silent again until he turns to me with a smile on his face.

"What?" I ask.

"D'you know, I think we've just been functioning from our positive 'Spontaneous Me's.' I've been real and you've been real and we've been sharing feelings," he says excitedly.

"Cool," I say blushing.

"Yeah, real cool," he says, grinning sheepishly at me.

Later when I snuggle down in my bed, Sharsha beside me, I smile to myself. Franklin's right. We *were* being truly intimate like Miss Tina talked about, not in a sexual way, but by being real with each other. I liked it. I didn't have to pretend anymore. I could be myself and know that I would be accepted for who I am. Awesome.

Franklin joins us girls at breakfast.

"Hi," he says to everyone. "Man, I'm tired, I was up all night with the baby," he quips.

I laugh and the others tell him he's goofy.

He walks with me to the Group Room. Miss Tina's already sitting in her chair, waiting for us. He sits next to me.

Everyone sits down and then shift their baby-selves into a comfortable position. It makes me smile.

Miss Tina breaks into my thoughts.

"Today we're going to look at another aspect of cutting... doing it for attention. Has anyone in this room ever cut so that they would get their parents' attention?"

She looks around the room. Two kids raise their hands gingerly and look embarrassed.

"That's how it started for me," a girl says honestly.

"Me, too," the other one adds.

"It can be a big problem," Miss Tina says seriously. "I have no doubt that kids who do this are driven by the same pent-up pressure and pain that has driven most of you to cut in the past. But these kids are not like you who cut in secret and do almost anything so that you're not discovered. Inadvertently, these kids learn that, when they cut, they get more attention than when they don't, and so in order to hold someone's attention, they cut more and more."

She shakes her head, looking as if she's in pain.

"These kids scare me to death, because the attention they get is dishonest, and it'll never be enough for them, so they're driven to cut more and more. Often they make increasingly more lethal cuts until one day they will kill themselves. Oh, they don't mean to die, but they're determined to hold their parents' attention. Letting out pent-up pressure and pain becomes secondary to their addiction... seeking their parents' attention. They do this because they don't believe they can get attention any other way, and in many instances they can't. That's what's so sad."

She's quiet for a moment; so are we. I've never cut for attention. I've always hidden it because I was ashamed of what I was doing. The two girls who owned up to cutting for attention look upset. I think they're awesome for being so honest, and I smile at them.

"Remember what I told you about some families having hidden rules that say, 'Don't feel anything.' Well, a child in a family like that would be very isolated. Think about it. When you share your emotions and feelings, you get loads of attention. Those who can't feel anything subconsciously seek another way to get the attention they need and deserve. Sometimes they play mind games, which are fairly harmless but stop them from being truly intimate with others from their 'Spontaneous Me's.'"

I glance at Franklin and he smiles at me.

"But other times things get more serious. If they cut and their parents get into a panic, not only will they get attention but they also learn that they can manipulate their parents. That's really bad, though, because the more a child can manipulate his parents, the more unsafe that child will feel. And the more unsafe that child feels, the more distress he will feel and the urge to cut will increase. Can you see how it's a vicious circle?"

She shakes her head again, and says, "You've no idea how sad it makes me feel, and how much it scares me, because a child like that will push and push, desperate to get more and more attention until one day he'll cut too hard and will die."

One of the girls who put her hand up speaks out.

"That's how it was for me. I felt awful all the time. My parents never gave me any attention; it was like I never existed. I hurt so badly inside. At first I started cutting to let my feelings out, but then when I noticed how much attention my parents gave me when they saw the blood, I got addicted to it. Every time they ignored me, or took me for granted, I cut myself, and they would stop what they were doing to give me some attention. After a while I felt hooked. I couldn't stop doing it. In the end I cut even though I didn't have any pent-up feelings to release."

"Thank you for being so honest, dear," Miss Tina says. "You've described perfectly how this can happen. What can adults do when faced with this situation so that they deal with it but don't reinforce it?"

"What does that mean?" Leisha asks.

"Reinforcing means, if I reward your behavior, you're more likely to repeat that behavior.

"So," Miss Tina continues, "if the parents, or whoever patches you up after you've cut yourself, show any kindness or concern, which of course they will, it will reinforce the cutting behaviour. How do you think adults should handle it?"

No one speaks.

"If a kid stands in front of me with blood dripping from his/her arms, my 'Nurturing Me' kicks in, which is what these kids are craving. But by being nurturing, I'm encouraging them to cut again. What can I do?" Miss Tina asks us again.

Macy speaks out. "I think you should clean up the mess and ignore it as much as you can, but give the kid attention for something else."

"Oh, Macy, you're so smart," Miss Tina says. "Yes, that's a good idea, because then you won't reinforce the cutting behavior, but you will reinforce safe behavior."

Macy beams.

"I have a story about all of this. It's about the hidden rule, 'Don't feel,' that's passed down from generation to generation, and how a child learns to get the only attention that's available to her. It shows you how it can happen, and how once you know these things, there's no blame, only understanding. Once you understand where everyone in the family's coming from, how can you feel blame? The story's called, 'The Vile Curse.'"

I shift in my chair and move Sharsha around so that we're comfortable. Miss Tina starts to read from some papers.

• • • •

Far, far away in the land that bobs in and out of view depending upon the sea mist, high up in the snow-covered mountains, there lived a princess. She lived with her parents, the king and queen. As a baby, Princess Joy had lain in her golden cradle alone beneath a vast portrait, which hung on the wall of the great hall. It was a picture of an ancient king and queen on their wedding day, both sitting on their thrones, rigid and unsmiling, their eyes cold and piercing. To the right of the portrait was a lectern with a great, golden book, not a Bible, but a book that told of the way to be, according to the ancient king and queen.

Some say that a cloud of joylessness shrouded the castle and all who lived in it, a legacy left from the icy, rigid king and queen who ruled hundreds of years ago, who watched from the great hall wall and whose words were spoken and followed through the ages.

The infant princess howled in her cradle, fear prickling along her spine beneath the ancient king and queen's frozen gaze, one that shriveled her sense of play and comfort. Her parents, who were also anxious beneath their gaze, left their beautiful daughter alone to cry, believing the words written in the great, golden book, "Don't be too close to other people, for they may steal your land and your worth." "Don't be concerned with feelings, for they are for fools and will weaken you," and "Don't allow your children to play and have fun, or you will lose control of them."

As Princess Joy grew up, she shivered beneath the piercing eyes of the king and queen in the portrait that seemed to follow her wherever she went... she was never free from their disapproval.

Deep within the castle, the king's cook poured

a cup of tea and spoke to the gardener and anyone that would listen to her.

"Tis a shame, no good will come of it. I remember when Princess Joy was a baby crying in her cradle, and the nurse begged to be allowed to pick her up, but the king and queen read from the great, golden book." She shook her head.

"They read, 'Don't be too close to other people, for they may steal your land and your worth.' 'Don't be concerned with feelings, for they are for fools and for the weak,' and 'Don't allow your children to play and have fun, or you will lose control of them.' What rubbish; that's what I say." She sounded angry and the gardener looked afraid.

"Don't let the king and queen hear you talk like that," the gardener said, "or they'll send us away and then what will become of our own children? We won't be able to feed and clothe them."

The cook was angry and slammed the pots and pans down, knowing that he was right.

"Doesn't mean I have to agree with them, does it?" she muttered. "It's a crying shame, that's what it is. Every child should be allowed to play and have fun, every child should know the joy of being close to others and feeling everything, good and bad, sweet and painful. How do you know if you're alive if you don't feel anything? I'll say it again, it's a crying shame, that's what it is."

She slammed her rolling pin down onto a lump

of pastry and began rolling with gusto. "What I'd like to do to all those kings and queens that have done nothing to lift the cloud of joylessness that hangs over this castle," she hissed.

The gardener left the kitchen, praying that she'd be quiet, for her words, although true, were dangerous. Once heard, they forced the listener to look deep into their hearts and question the words written in the great, golden book. He knew she was right, but he was afraid.

Princess Joy looked out of the castle window with pain in her heart as she watched the servants' children darting around the castle grounds, laughing and playing. How she longed to join them, but she knew that it was impossible. She had asked years ago and suffered her parents' disapproval as they read from the great, golden book that told of how one should be, and their displeasure had shriveled her heart further.

So the cloud of joylessness continued to darken the castle and their hearts. Not even the cook's efforts to please Princess Joy made her smile, for over time she had forgotten how to smile. Deep within her was a well of pain, one that was so deep that she couldn't remember how it had begun or imagine where it would end. As the well of pain became deeper and deeper, a terrible and vile curse came upon the princess, one more terrible than all the writings of the great, golden book and one more terrible than the cloud of joylessness.

It happened by accident one day when Princess Joy had tried to peel an apple. The royal knife had slipped and sliced into her finger. Vivid red blood sprang from the wound, and the princess was so shocked that she just stood and stared at the crimson bead as it grew and dripped to the floor. Something unfamiliar happened to her, something awful but new; for the first time in her life, she felt something.

The writings of the great, golden book were so ingrained into her that she didn't know it was possible to feel anything, so as the stinging in her finger intensified, she rejoiced. Never had she known anything like it, but she was unaware of the creeping, insidious nature of this terrible, vile curse. For although she rejoiced in feeling something, anything, the vile curse took hold of her in an unrelenting, vice-like grip.

It was like a vile odor, one that poisoned and suffocated the living. It's creeping tentacles ensnared her, for as the blood dripped upon the polished castle floor, the king and queen were awakened from the teachings of the great, golden book telling how one should be, and they began to show their feelings of concern for their beautiful daughter.

Never had Princess Joy experienced such attention, and as she bathed in their concern, the vile curse was strengthened, for it was only when the princess hurt herself that she received the love she longed for, which is every child's birthright. Day after day the princess sought the comfort of knowing that her parents cared about her, and as she saw the concern in their eyes while she bled, the curse took hold of her and her fate was sealed.

The cook and gardener wrung their hands as they watched the tragedy unfold. The princess and her parents were locked into a drama that had no solution in the writings of the great, golden book.

The vile curse gripped the castle. The king and queen were in despair not knowing what to do, and being subject to the great, golden book, they were dumbfounded by feelings that they too had never known before. They didn't know how to be close to each other or how to feel the gift that the gods had given them merely because they were human — the gift of feeling. And as their beautiful daughter became addicted to feeling something, anything, she hurt herself more and more.

Yet the vile curse had a wicked twist. It tricked the beautiful princess. Each time she hurt herself and experienced the joy of feeling, she saw the despair in her parents' hearts, their anger and their inability to understand her, or reach her. Rather than release the pain of emptiness within her, the well of pain became deeper and deeper until she could hardly bear it anymore. So in her despair, she did the only thing that she knew how to do: She hurt herself more, believing that it would lessen her pain. Deep within her a voice screamed in silence to be heard but was drowned out by the vile curse and by the teachings of the great, golden book.

No one knew that the vile curse had almost wended its way, its path leading to oblivion, the darkness of death. For although each person in the castle from king to cook despaired watching the tragedy unfold, none knew how to stop it or how to choose another path.

None felt the despair as much as the cook, whose own children knew the gifts of laughter, of fun, of feelings and of being close to one another, and as she watched the vile curse take hold of the castle, her anger grew.

"Be careful," warned the gardener. "If you speak your mind, they'll send us away; then where will we be?"

"I don't care. It's getting worse. The vile curse is determined to kill Princess Joy and I will not stand by and watch it happen. Help me to do something," she begged the gardener.

"But what?"

She wrung her hands and admitted that she didn't know what to do.

"I can tell Princess Joy how beautiful she is, but what good will that do? It's not from me that she needs to hear it, but from the king and queen. And how can they tell her what they feel if they are influenced by the great, golden book, which tells them that they shouldn't feel, shouldn't be close to anyone and shouldn't have fun or play..."

"... And that horrid portrait," the gardener said, shivering at the thought. "It watches me wherever I go, and their faces are so full of disapproval that it makes me feel quite crumpled and worthless."

That night the pain in Princess Joy's heart was so excruciating when she saw the anger and anxiety in the king and queen's faces, that she locked herself in her palatial bathroom and hurt herself so badly that death's claws gripped her. She lay on the floor, alone and cold, her well of pain deeper than ever while her parents went to bed believing that she had also gone to bed.

Life slipped away from her, and the vile curse laughed as it stepped up to claim her.

And it would have if it hadn't been for the Gods of the Trees, who know what's inside every living creature's heart. As Princess Joy's spirit was about to join those who float among the trees, a great howl of anger blew through the woods causing the gardener to pull on his coat and leave his house to check his plants.

"Something's not right," he muttered to himself as he hurried up to the kitchen door. "Something's not right, I just know it."

The cook was still up, making royal muffins for the king and queen's breakfast.

"Something's not right," the gardener spat out, trying to catch his breath. "The trees and the wind are acting funny; something's not right."

The cook listened, and she too heard the Gods of the Trees howling in the night for the life of the beautiful princess who had almost succumbed to the vile curse.

She ran up the stone steps two at a time and didn't knock at Princess Joy's door but burst in, knowing that something terrible had happened. She was too fearful to cry, although she longed to, for she knew the gift of feeling and of being close to other people. As she burst into the princess's bathroom and found her pale and lifeless body on the cold stone floor, she gasped with fear.

She cradled Princess Joy in her arms, crooning in her ear, rocking her gently, telling her how beautiful and how special she was, oblivious to the gardener, who had awakened the king and queen. They were standing in the doorway, along with all the servants and the royal cats.

The Gods of the Trees stopped howling and a calm came over the castle in the mountains. Princess Joy, hearing the crooning lilt of the cook's voice, felt soothed and comforted, and for the first time in her life the well of pain began to lessen. As it did, the vile curse was sucked out of the castle and was blown away by the Gods of the Trees, whose anger knows no bounds.

The king and queen wrang their hands in despair, not knowing what to do, still being under the spell of the great, golden book. They had no idea how to behave in the same way as the cook — although they longed to, for they loved their beautiful daughter with all their hearts.

The cook looked at them, at first with fear in her heart, wondering if they were going to banish her from the castle. But as they edged forward, she smiled and gently placed the princess, who was still very pale and close to death, in their arms.

"Like this," she said gently. "Show her you love her like this."

And so the king and queen held their daughter and for the first time in their lives knew the feeling of closeness and joy, as they had named their beautiful girl. A tear ran down the king's cheek and he felt afraid. He didn't know how to experience feelings and it felt strange and frightening to him, but he was brave and sat with his feelings until they became less scary to him.

A new day dawned, one where the vile curse could never enter the castle again, for something more wonderful happened that morning.

The gardener, who did odd jobs around the castle, climbed a ladder in the great hall in order to paint the ceiling. He had a large pot of paint balanced on top of the ladder, and he whistled while he worked.

"Would you like a cup of tea?" called the cook, and being startled, the gardener yelled in fright and lost his footing. He wobbled and grabbed at the ladder, knocking the paint pot over, and crashed to the floor.

"Ahhh," he cried. "Oh, heavens, now I'm in trouble."

The paint splattered all over the portrait of the ancient king and queen sitting upon their thrones, their austerity and coldness hidden by dribbles of paint that ran towards the floor.

"Quick, grab something to help me clean it up," he said and frantically began wiping the paint from the portrait. But as he wiped, the paint was spread further and further over the portrait until there was nothing left of the ancient king and queen, whose frozen gaze had withered the hearts of those before them.

The gardener shook in dismay at the sight before him, but that was nothing compared to what he did when he realized what was in his hand... he had torn pages from the great, golden book and had used them as cleaning cloths!

"Oh, my," said the cook, with a smile on her face. "Oops."

To the amazement of the gardener, who was sure that he would be banished from the castle for having destroyed the portrait and words of the ancestors, nothing happened. And he felt sure he saw a faint smile on the king and queen's lips when he tried to explain. Princess Joy, held for the first time by her parents who had always loved her but just didn't know how to show it, grew strong and she never, ever needed to hurt herself again in order to feel. Her parents learned from the cook and the gardener how to feel and to be close to one another and most of all how to have fun and play. Little by little the castle was filled with laughter and joy, and the little princess knew her name and all that it meant.

One day when the snows had melted and flowers pushed their way through the earth to the warm rays of sun, the gardener showed Princess Joy how to dig up a patch of earth to plant her favorite flowers.

"You know, in days of old and when the Gods of the Trees ruled this earth, this ground was considered sacred."

"Oh?" she said, raking through the loose earth.

"Yes, it's said that hidden in this sacred land is the answer."

"The answer to what?" Princess Joy asked.

"The answer to everything."

They grew silent for a while as each carried on digging and raking, enjoying the scent of the flowers on the breeze, the birdsong and insects scurrying to find their homes, when Princess Joy suddenly called out.

"What's that?" she cried, her fork hitting something solid.

The gardener used his hands to clean off the earth from a tablet of stone, his eyes wide, not having really believed that the land was sacred.

"It's a tablet of stone," his voice trembled with excitement, and his hands shook as he lifted the stone out of the ground.

"What does it say?" asked Princess Joy.

He was quiet for a moment as the cook walked up behind them with a tray of freshly baked cookies.

"What's that?" she asked

"It's the answer," the gardener breathed, with awe in his voice.

"What does it say?" Princess Joy and the cook said together.

He paused for a moment and then said quietly, "There is no blame, only understanding."

● ● ● ●

Miss Tina puts down the papers and looks at us.

"Although some of you have been hurt by your parents' inability to show their feelings, don't *blame* them. Try to *understand* why they are that way. They learned from their parents, who learned from their parents before them and so on. When you understand, you can change things so that when *you* become parents, your child won't experience the same hidden 'Don't feel' rule."

Chapter Eleven

We spend the afternoon resting and growing, lying on the beach in the sun. I feel overdressed with my long-sleeved shirt on.

"Why don't you go and change your shirt?" Macy asks. I wince. "It's okay, we're all the same here. We've all got scars."

"I haven't got any short-sleeved tops."

"C'mon, you can borrow one of mind."

Macy jumps up and grabs my hand, pulling me to my feet. My baby-self nearly falls to the ground but I grab her and settle her back into the sling. I follow Macy over the sand and across the playground. We go up the spiral staircase towards her room.

"Come in," she says, as I stand at her door. She goes over to her closet and sifts through her clothes. "Here, how about this?"

She holds up a halter neck top.

"No, too revealing."

"How about this shirt then?" She holds up a shirt with no sleeves. "You'll feel nice and cool in this."

My stomach churns with anxiety.

"I don't know," I say. "I don't know if I'm ready for this. I feel ashamed of my scars."

Macy throws the shirt at me. "C'mon, Marsha, you've got to do it some time; why not now? No one here will judge you, you know that. They'll respect your bravery. Give me your baby-self while you change, okay?"

She doesn't take "No" for an answer and steps up to take Sharsha from me. Reluctantly I slip the sling over my shoulder and hand Sharsha to her. She makes me giggle when she makes high-pitched cooing baby noises at her. I take my shirt off and slip into Macy's sleeveless one.

"The color suits you," she says.

I stand with my arms crossed over my chest. I feel ashamed. She walks over to me, and with Sharsha in one arm, she pulls at one of my hands with her other. She looks into my face, and tears spring into my eyes.

"Each one tells a story, huh?"

I nod.

She gives me a hug with her free arm, and her baby-self gets squashed between us.

"Oops, sorry," she says into her sling. "Here, Sharsha misses her mommy."

"I'm not her mommy," I say. "I'm her."

"Oh, yeah. Sorry, I got carried away."

I nestle Sharsha squarely next to me in her sling.

"Are you ready?" Macy asks. I nod. "C'mon then. Let's go."

I follow her down the stairs, feeling naked and awful. My arms, although they've healed, look like a badly sewn patchwork quilt. I feel sick. I lag behind as she heads towards the door onto the playground, but then she gets behind me and pushes me outside.

I wrap my arms around Sharsha and hold her tight. I feel small and vulnerable, and very afraid. I imagine Sharsha's afraid and crying, in the same way Casey and Shelley used to cry when they were babies and Mom ignored them, and something very powerful comes over me. Suddenly I feel strong. I hold her tightly and, even though I don't say it aloud, I tell her in my head that she'll be all right. I follow Macy through the playground and across the sand to where the kids are hanging out. They look up as we flop down on the sand.

Franklin and Greg are skimming stones at the water's edge. The girls look at me, and Leisha says, "Hey girl, no way. You beat me. I was going to be the next one to reveal."

She reaches over and gives me a high-five. My fear dissolves instantly.

"Right, that's it," she says. "You may have

beaten me, but I'm going to beat Poppy."

"No way," Poppy yells.

They embark upon a crazy race to roll their sleeves up and expose their scars.

I can't help myself, I giggle at the sight of them fumbling to free their thumbs and roll their sleeves tight enough so that they'll stay up.

Macy shouts, "Go, go, go."

Franklin and Greg come over to us and sit down. Franklin sits next to me and Macy digs me in the ribs, grinning. I shoot her a warning glance.

"Hey," says Greg. "What's going on?"

Macy says, "Marsha 'revealed' and beat these two."

"I didn't realize it was a race," I say.

"Well, Candy and I had a sort of bet as to who'd be brave enough to go sleeveless," Macy says.

I smile at her. I wouldn't have done it if she hadn't nagged me to do it. I'm glad. "Thanks," I mouth at her, and she waves me away with her hand.

"Anyone for another baby race along the beach?" Greg asks.

"No way," Candy says. "I heard Ken talking about someone in reception complaining about us having upset their kids." She snorts, unable to stop the grin that slides onto her face. "We'd better not."

"Shame," Greg says, pretending to be devastated. "It was a blast."

We get quiet. Yes, it was funny, but I felt weird

afterwards, as if I hadn't taken care of myself. I don't want to laugh about it, because it doesn't feel right somehow. The others don't laugh either, and I wonder if they're thinking the same.

"Oh well, another time," he says.

Franklin looks at me, and there's something in his face that anchors me back to what we talked about in the playground. I work up the courage to say what's on my mind.

"Greg, I know you don't like babies, so how do you feel about your baby-self? Is it having an effect on you like it is on me?"

Greg looks at me, and I shield my eyes from the sun, trying to figure out what's on his face.

He seems to dodge the question.

"So it's having an effect on you then?"

"Yes, a big effect. How about you?"

He stares out to sea, and suddenly he's serious. "D'you want to know what effect it's having on me? I feel stupid because I can't feel anything, and I feel even worse when I see that it's having a big effect on all of you. I don't know how to do it, okay?"

Candy puts her hand on his shoulder, and says, "I think it takes practice, that's all. If you like babies, it's easy, but if you don't like them, just keep telling yourself that your baby-self is you."

He shrugs and we are quiet. He gets up and goes inside.

We look at each other not knowing what to say.

Macy gets up.

"I'll go after him," she says.

I feel awful for having asked him how he felt, and I say so, but the others shout me down and tell me not to be silly.

"That's what we do here," Candy says. "We talk about difficult things and sometimes it hurts."

I don't feel like hanging out anymore so I get up and go inside, too. One by one the others follow me. I go through the double doors and bump into Miss Tina.

"What's wrong?" she asks me.

"I think I upset Greg." I feel tears prick my eyes. "I really like him, and I feel bad."

"What happened?"

"I asked him if carrying his baby-self was having an effect on him even though he doesn't like babies. He got upset."

"Don't worry about it, Marsha. We'll deal with it in group later, okay?" She smiles at me and looks at my bare arms. "I'm so proud of you," she says.

For a moment I wonder what she's talking about. I shake my head, my feelings of concern for Greg overpowering my shame at my naked arms.

I spend the rest of the afternoon on my bed with my headphones on. Sometimes I sing along, although I can't hear myself. I take Sharsha out of her sling and sit her on my stomach and I stroke her hair. Her eyes penetrate mine, and when I move, they seem to follow me. Her smile is so cute. I feel a weird sense of love for her, and as I think it, I correct myself... I feel a weird sense of love for *me*.

Macy pokes her head around my door and I pull my headphones out of my ears.

"What?" I shout.

"I could hear you singing all the way down the hall," she laughs. "It's time for group."

I slip Sharsha back into her sling and follow Macy down the stairs.

Greg is already in the Group Room. I can't read what's on his face. I feel awkward.

Miss Tina waits until we're all sitting down before speaking.

"Marsha and Greg come here."

I feel sick, but I go towards her. She smiles at us. "Don't look so worried," she says to me. She drops two large cushions on the floor in front of her and tells us each to sit on one.

"Marsha, say what's on your mind to Greg," she demands.

I feel nervous and I don't want to say anything, but everyone's watching so I say, "Greg, I'm sorry if I upset you somehow. I was really interested to find out whether carrying your baby-self around was having the same effect on you as it is on me, even though you don't like babies."

He shakes his head.

"You haven't done anything to upset me. I've

upset myself. I look at all of you with your *babies* and because *I* don't feel anything, I think there's something wrong with me."

He looks around the room.

"I want to feel the same thing you're all feeling, but I can't and I don't know why."

I feel braver.

"I wanted to know whether not liking babies would stop you from seeing your doll as your 'Spontaneous Me.' I was interested, that's all."

Miss Tina smiles at us and says, "Y'know, it's an interesting question, Greg. Remember I said that human beings are programmed to nurture infant creatures; if you find it difficult to respond to infants, it's likely that you have *learned* to block that instinct."

She looks around the room and says, "What we need to do is to help Greg tap into his 'Nurturing Me,' because that's what this is all about. Okay, babies won't do it for him, but there has to be another way. It doesn't really matter what object you use to help you *see* your 'Spontaneous Me' as being a real, separate entity that you have to take care of. You can choose anything so long as it hooks into your 'Nurturing Me.' That's the whole point."

There's a knock on the door and Ken comes into the room. He sits next to Miss Tina and they share a smile. He's wearing a jacket, and he keeps looking inside it. I wonder if he's got his new baby snuggled up inside.

Miss Tina tells me to go back to my chair. I'm glad.

Ken sits on my cushion opposite Greg.

Miss Tina says, "Greg, give me your baby-self."

He fumbles in the sling tied around his body and hands the doll, that looks so much like him, to Miss Tina. He holds his baby-self by the arm, as if it's something alien to him. I feel sad. I could never handle Sharsha like that. I hold her tighter to me and watch what's going to happen.

Miss Tina puts his baby-self over her shoulder and starts to pat its butt. It's like even though *he* refuses to take care of his true self, she will. She says, "Greg, I want you to think about Philip Pullman's story, remember, the English author, who wrote about a world where each person's soul lived outside their bodies in the shape of an animal. It was impossible to hurt the creature that represented their true selves, the part of themselves that was present at birth before they modified themselves to fit into their families. Close your eyes."

Miss Tina steps towards Ken and some of the girls gasp when she reaches into his jacket and pulls out a beautiful, tiny puppy. She opens Greg's sling and slips the puppy into it. His eyes pop open immediately.

I sit holding Sharsha, struggling with my own feelings as I watch Greg try to understand what's happening.

His hands cradle the puppy outside the sling and something amazing happens to his face. His stress melts away and his jaw softens. He slips a hand into the sling, and when the puppy licks his fingers, he laughs gently so as not to frighten it. I swallow hard. I know Sharsha isn't real, but if she were that's how I'd treat her, too. As the thought pops into my head, I understand what's going on. Greg can't see his baby-self in the form of a doll like the rest of us can, and so Miss Tina has made it more real for him by making his baby-self a real live creature. And it's working. Greg seems lost in his own little world where the only thing that matters is the vulnerable, defenseless little puppy in his sling.

Miss Tina kneels down on the floor, and says, "Greg, you have to see yourself like this beautiful, spontaneous puppy... precious, full of fun, yet vulnerable. When you can do this, you'll be able to take care of yourself forever more. You'll *never* cut yourself again. How could you hurt this beautiful creature?"

He scoops the puppy out of the sling and cradles it in his hands and kisses its nose. Then he puts it on his chest and strokes its back. Greg seems different. He's quiet and calm. Suddenly he looks like Franklin taking care of Frankie, and he looks like me taking care of Sharsha. Miss Tina and Ken have just shown him how to hook into his "Nurturing Me."

"Do whatever it takes," Miss Tina says, "to hook

your 'Nurturing Me' into taking care of your 'Spontaneous Me' so that you'll never *ever* hurt yourselves again, okay?"

"Okay," we say as one.

"Go and sit down, Greg, and take care of Little Greg."

He slips the puppy into his sling and carefully gets up. The girls sitting on either side of him coo over the puppy whose nose is poking out of the sling, sniffing.

Miss Tina says, "Let's think about what you're going to do when you leave here. You won't be able to carry your baby-self around with you or the kids at school will think you've lost your mind." She grins at us. "But I'm hoping that by keeping your baby-self with you all the time while you're here in this safe place, you'll get used to tapping into your 'Nurturing Me.' Then, when you leave here, you'll be able to visualize your baby-self if the addictive urge to cut comes over you. *Seeing* your baby-self in your mind will keep you safe."

Ken leaves the room.

Miss Tina says, "Okay, let's talk about coping with your scars. Marsha, Leisha and Poppy, I'm so proud of you for baring your arms. How did it make you feel?"

"Scared," I say. "I felt ashamed of myself and afraid that other people would judge me."

"No one will judge you here," Miss Tina says.

"But it's a sad fact that people outside Beach Haven *will* judge you. Y'know, people judge others all the time. When you first meet someone, within seconds you've formed an opinion based initially on what you see and how a person behaves. Your opinion will reflect your beliefs; that's how stereotypes are formed. We all do it to a certain extent, and often our judgment is wrong.

"I had a friend who covered his body with tattoos. He was a kind, gentle human being who just loved body art. When I met him, he was new to the area and was trying to meet people, so he went to church. It was summer and he wore a short-sleeved shirt, but when he held out his hand, people shunned him."

"That's sick," Greg says angrily.

"It's not good, is it? But he had a choice at that point. He could forgive other people's misconceptions and ignorance, or he could pick himself up and try to reach out again. He could tell himself that the people weren't ready to understand his body art, so, in order to help them, he could cover his art with long sleeves. He went to another church, wearing long sleeves and was welcomed, and made many friends. Once they had come to really know him, he was able to show them his body art and explain what all of it meant to him."

I think I see what Miss Tina's getting at.

"It's like that for you. You have a choice. You can

reveal your scars or hide them, but without being ashamed. If you choose to wear short sleeves, be prepared for some people to stare. Have an answer ready if they should ask what happened to you. Depending upon how you feel, you can tell them you've been on a long and painful journey, but you're very proud of yourself for working through it. If you don't want to explain yourself, you can just say, 'It's a long story.' Or you could joke by saying, 'I had a fight with Edward Scissorhands, and you should see how *he* ended up,' which is a polite way of telling them to mind their own business."

We laugh.

"Scars will fade in time, although they'll never go away completely."

"I thought you could have laser treatments to get rid of them," Poppy says, "although it's expensive, my mom said."

Miss Tina agrees, "Yes, there are some laser treatments that'll help reduce the scars, but they won't get rid of them completely. But as technology progresses, who knows, maybe in the future the treatments will be better. The point I want to make is this; are you going to allow your scars to stop you from succeeding in life and being happy? Will you allow the consequences of this difficult period in your life ruin your future? You have to think positively."

Leisha sounds sad. "I understand everything you're saying, but I feel angry and sad at the same time."

"Say why."

"I feel angry with myself for having made such a mess of my arms. Look at them," she says, thrusting them out for us to see. They *are* a mess. "And then I feel sad because I feel like I've messed up my life. What am I going to do at the senior prom? All my friends will be wearing beautiful dresses and I'll be stuck in some nerdy long-sleeved top, and that's how it's going to be forever."

She cries and I feel like crying, too. That's how it's going to be for me as well. I'll never be able to wear the type of beautiful dresses you see film stars wearing on TV either.

"It's all right for guys, because they can wear a suit and no one would ever know they had a problem. It's not fair," Leisha adds, sniffing.

Miss Tina smiles at us and says, "Don't you worry. I have a plan. Guys, you're excused from this. Bye!"

Greg and Franklin look confused, but they get up and leave the room along with the other guys.

Miss Tina grins, and says, "Come with me."

We follow her along the corridor to Miss Cassie's classroom. When we go inside, Miss Cassie's standing by a big table in the middle of the room, and it's covered with reams of different colored fabric.

"Hello, girls. I'm going to show you how to make your dress for the Beach Haven graduation prom."

We all start talking at once, but she talks over our chatter.

"C'mon, choose a pattern and the fabric you like."

There are several patterns on the table, and all are strappy, sleeveless dresses.

Leisha turns to Miss Tina and says, "But I can't wear something like this; I'd be ashamed. I can't do it."

Miss Cassie smiles as Miss Tina answers her. "Yes, you can. Trust me, I have a plan. Just make your dresses and then I'll show you, okay?"

"Okay."

I've never made anything before, let alone a prom dress.

Miss Cassie calls out, "Ignore your arms; just choose the dress of your dreams."

So I do. It's backless except for criss-cross spaghetti straps. It's fitted and has a split up the back. It's gorgeous. I ignore the nagging doubt in my mind that tells me I could never wear such a dress because of my mutilated arms, and I let the girls' excited chatter chase my thoughts away.

"Look at this one," Macy says, "It's heavenly."

"Yeah, but look at this one," Leisha cries. "It's divine. Look at the skirt."

Candy grabs a pattern and her eyes are wide. "Can you imagine wearing a dress like this?"

Miss Cassie says, "You don't have to imagine, child, just do it."

Candy's face lights up and she says, "Then I'm having this one."

"Oh my," Poppy says, "do you think I'd look good in this if I breathe in?" She turns sideways and presses her hands against her stomach and butt.

"Okay, girls," Miss Cassie says. "Now choose the fabric you want your dress to be made out of."

The table is awash with colors, but there's only one choice for me. I want a black dress, classy and elegant. I tell Miss Cassie what I want.

She retrieves the black fabric from the table and pins a label to it with my name on. Macy chooses a chocolate brown to match her eyes. Leisha chooses pink, while Candy opts for silver. Poppy goes for the red.

Miss Cassie tells us to sit down. We sit around the big table and it's hard to concentrate. I shift Sharsha around so that the knot from her sling, which is digging into my shoulder blade, isn't so uncomfortable. Miss Cassie looks as excited as we are.

"Over the next two weeks you are going to learn how to make your dress. I'll help you. I don't expect you to do the difficult bits, but you're going to learn how to sew. It's fun. Once you learn, you can make anything and know that you can attend a dance or an important dinner wearing something that no other living soul is wearing."

"How did you learn to sew?" Candy asks.

"When I was at school." She seems to drift off. "I was ten years old and we had to make an apron. I remember being terrified as we lined up to show the head teacher our work. She was scary. I'd tried so hard to hem my apron properly, but she told me my stitches were clumsy — too big — and I felt crushed. I thought I was useless at sewing, but at high school I learned more, and I wanted to make the type of gowns that film stars wear." She shrugs and smiles at us. "But then I started to work at Beach Haven and found that working with kids was more important than making glitsy gowns."

My heart swells; I like her.

"But now," she says, alive with passion, "I get to care about all of you *and* make glitsy gowns! Okay, you've all chosen your patterns and your fabric so tonight I'm going to cut out the pieces and have them ready for you to work on tomorrow."

"I've never made anything in my life, except a mess," Poppy says.

I say that I've never made anything either. I don't believe that I can make a dress like the one shown on the pattern.

"You aren't going to do it alone. I'm going to show you how to do it, and you're going to do the bits you can do, and I'll do the bits you can't do, but you'll watch and learn, okay?"

"Okay," we say.

I'll do whatever she tells me to do. I want to learn, and I want to know what it feels like to stand in front of a mirror dressed like a film star.

Miss Cassie tells us to put our baby-selves on the table because she wants to measure us. I prop Sharsha up against Macy's Maemae.

Miss Cassie has a tape measure around her neck and tells us to form a line. One by one she measures every part of us and writes it down. I breathe in when she measures me, but she takes so long that I exhale.

"Stop it," she laughs. "Be yourself. Stand still."

I do as she says while Leisha stands behind me and tells me to hurry up. I can tell she's excited.

When Miss Cassie finishes taking measurements, she tells us all to sit. We do as she asks and wait to hear what she has to say.

I'm already excited but then she says, "The boys don't know about the Beach Haven graduation prom, it's a secret. Don't let them know anything about it, okay? We want to wow them, don't we?"

"Yes," Leisha says.

"Yes," we all say.

"Good," says Miss Cassie. "We've got a lot of work to do, and I expect you to be here as much as you can."

My head is spinning with excitement. As she talks, I'm aware that she's coming from her "Controlling Me" at first, but when I look at her I see that she's switched to her "Spontaneous Me" because it's clear that she's enjoying herself.

Chapter Twelve

We go to bed excited. Franklin catches up with me and asks if I want to hang out for a while. I'm so excited about my dress and the prom that I don't trust myself. I know I'll give it away if I hang out with him. He and I have connected from our "Spontaneous Me's" and I know that he'll figure it out if I'm lying. He looks confused when I tell him I'm tired but rush off to join the other girls, who seem to feel the same as I do. We don't want to be around the boys right now. We've got a secret.

I take Sharsha out of her sling and set her next to me in bed. I get up several times because I'm too excited about the prom to be able to sleep. I open my window and climb back into bed, listening to the ocean rolling up the sand just yards away from my window. I can smell the salt in the air. I pull Sharsha towards me. Her presence makes me feel complete.

It's a strange feeling, but every night when I go to bed I feel a bit different from how I was the night before. Tonight I feel excited. I'm going to learn how to make something gorgeous. I'm irritated that I have to sleep. I want to do it now. It's hours before sleep settles over me.

I awaken with Sharsha nestled next to me, and her presence makes me feel great.

My alarm rings; I have to get up. I hug Sharsha and put her on my bed so that I can take my shower. I towel myself dry and slip into my jeans. I can't wear Macy's sleeveless top again, so I put on one of my long-sleeved tops and meticulously turn up the sleeves. I stand in front of the mirror to make sure they're even, and when I'm satisfied, I slip my sling on and place Sharsha into it. I adjust the knot that rests on my shoulder blade so that it's as comfortable as it can be. A thought pops into my mind... perhaps the sling isn't supposed to be comfortable; it's there as a constant reminder to take care of ourselves.

When I walk into the dining room I can sense an atmosphere immediately. We girls have a secret and the boys can tell. They want to know what it is, but no one's telling. A giggle struggles to get loose from behind my stoic face.

Franklin joins me as I fill my plate with pancakes, syrup and sausage.

"What happened last night after Miss Tina told

us to leave?" he asks me.

A nervous giggle threatens to betray me. I clear my throat and act as best I can.

"Oh, nothing. Miss Tina thought that we should learn to sew, that's all."

"To *sew*?" he asks incredulously. I know he doesn't believe me, even though it's partially the truth.

"Yeah, she thinks we should learn to sew. It's a girlie thing, I think," I say, knowing that I'm manipulating him in order to keep our secret safe.

"Marsha, you know that's sexist," Franklin says, and I swear I see a look of disappointment on his face.

"Oh, I don't mean it like that," I say, trying to backtrack so that he'll still think I'm cool.

After breakfast Miss Tina tells the boys that the Group Room needs painting, and Ken's going to show them how to do it. We girls head straight for Miss Cassie's classroom.

Miss Cassie has put a sewing machine on each table. She tells us to sit around the big table next to a pile of cut-out fabric with our pattern resting on top of it.

"Right, what you have to do first is to practice on your sewing machines. Here's some spare fabric for you to practice getting your seams straight. Everything you have to do I'm going to show you first."

We spend all morning learning how to thread our machines, sewing in a straight line, matching notches and tacking pieces of fabric together, ironing seams flat, and making darts so that the fabric turns into a different shape.

"Good job," Miss Cassie says when it's lunchtime. "This afternoon we'll start on your dresses."

I feel a bit nervous; what if I get it wrong?

We sit in the dining room talking excitedly but get quiet when the boys come into the room.

"What's up with you girls?" Greg asks. "Were you talking about us?"

"No," we all say at once, which makes it sound like we were. I giggle; I can't help it.

Greg looks mad and walks over to the table to fill his plate. He feeds tidbits to Little Greg, who's sniffing wildly as he smells the food.

He and Franklin sit at the next table, and we sit in silence until everyone's finished eating.

"Hey," Greg says indignantly as we get up. "What's going on?"

"Nothing," we say, as we head outside onto the playground.

Ten minutes later the boys join us. Franklin sits next to me. He's got spots of paint all over his face. He looks funny.

"You've got paint on your face," I tell him.

"Where?"

"Everywhere."

I pick it off for him and he smiles at me. Being close to him gives me butterflies in my stomach.

"How did your sewing class go?"

"Keep still," I say, changing the subject as I pick at his face. "It looks like you had fun painting."

"Yeah, it was okay. It was a bit boring having to sand the woodwork down, but the painting part was good." He becomes quiet for a moment. "Marsha, *were* you talking about us before we walked into the dining room?"

"No," I answer honestly.

He frowns at me.

"What?"

He bites his lip. "You seem different."

"Different than what?" I stall.

"Different than how you were the other night. I'm confused. It feels like you're not being *real*."

My stomach flips over.

"The other night I really felt that you were being real with me, but now I don't."

I don't know what to say, and he takes my silence the wrong way.

"Oh, I get it," he says, and walks off.

Tears spring into my eyes. Leisha comes over to me.

"What's up, girl?"

I'm annoyed with myself as the tears roll down my face.

"Franklin's mad at me. I like him, and the other

night we got along really well. You know what Miss Tina said about true intimacy, being *real* with someone else, well, I felt that with Franklin," I sniff. "But he *knows* I'm holding out on him. I think he thinks I don't like him, but I can't tell him that the reason I'm being secretive is just because of the prom."

She digs into her pocket and hands me a tissue.

"Forget it, girl. Maybe he's being a bit too sensitive. I mean, it's hard to be full-on real all the time," she says wisely. "That would be exhausting."

She takes my hand and pulls me up. "C'mon, let's go and get our toes wet."

It's high tide and the waves rush up the shore and come almost to the playground. We kick off our shoes and wade in the warm water as it swirls around our ankles.

Later I pass Franklin in the corridor, and he says, "Hi," but doesn't smile. I feel crushed. I go to Miss Cassie's classroom and spend the afternoon marking out the darts on the front and back of my dress with a chalk pencil. Miss Cassie watches over everything we do and goes from table to table guiding us. Gingerly I feed the fabric through the sewing machine, taking care to sew on the lines I've drawn, but my heart's not in it. I feel like a black cloud has descended on me, and I don't know how to shake it off.

It stays with me all day, through dinner, when Franklin sits on the opposite side of the room, and when we hang out in the living room watching a movie. I can't concentrate, so I go to bed and hold Sharsha close to me, trying to gain some comfort from her, trying to tap into my "Nurturing Me."

As the days pass and our dresses take shape, Franklin still ignores me, and my sadness turns to anger. I haven't done anything wrong except keep a secret. Everyone's allowed to have a good secret. I don't have to be like a goldfish bowl with everything inside me on display in order to be *real* with someone else. Surely I can choose what I share, can't I? I talk it over with the girls when we hang out on the beach, the girls in one group and the guys some way off in another.

We haven't had any groups since we started making our dresses, and the guys have been decorating the Group Room, so the distance between us gets worse. I don't know what to do because to try and explain why we're being evasive will give away our secret. As we slip into two separate groups, I realize that we're functioning from our negative "Modified Me's" and we should get ourselves into our "Thinking Me's" and talk about what's going on. But I don't know how to do it without ruining the surprise. Now I see how people can fall out when they can't talk things through. I think about my mom and dad. I bet they've never talked out their problems, although they might be able to now that they know about their "Thinking Me's."

After two weeks our dresses are almost finished; they look awesome. All I have to do on mine is to hem it. We sit around the big table hemming our dresses by hand — it takes forever — but Miss Cassie says that the dresses will hang better if we do it by hand. She shows us how, and I rest my dress on Sharsha and rethread my needle as I run out of thread. When I finish, Miss Cassie shows me how to press the hem so that it'll hang properly, and I do it really carefully.

I feel excited as I hang up my dress. It looks amazing. I can't believe that *I* made it. I still feel nervous about wearing it with my scars showing, but I remember that Miss Tina said that she's got a plan.

The prom is tomorrow, and I wonder what the guys will say when they're told.

"What's going on?" Greg asks during dinner as we chatter quietly among ourselves and giggle excitedly.

"Oh, you'll see," Poppy says.

"Whatever!" he says, from his "Modified Me."

I go to bed early because I can't stand the stress.

After lunch the next day Miss Tina calls us into the Group Room.

"It looks cool," Candy says as we go through the door.

"Yes," Miss Tina says, "the guys did a good job."

The boys sit on one side of the room, and we girls sit on the other.

"What's going on?" Miss Tina asks.

We sit there in silence for a moment, looking anywhere other than at Miss Tina. As I glance around, I catch Franklin's eye and look away quickly. This all started with him.

I speak out. "This mess all started when Franklin accused me of not being *real* with him."

"Is that right, Franklin?" Miss Tina asks him.

He speaks up for himself.

"It all started after one night when Marsha and I talked. We understood what you said about 'true intimacy,' oh, not sex," he adds, as Greg raises an eyebrow. "I was being real with Marsha and she was being real with me. It felt great. We were functioning from our 'Spontaneous Me's' and it felt awesome. It blew me away a bit, as I'd never felt it before."

He swallows hard.

"Then a few days later the girls seemed to be different, secretive and giggly. I asked Marsha what was going on, but she wouldn't tell me. I'm not stupid, y'know, and I could tell that she wasn't being *real* with me. Having felt what it's like to be real with someone, it seems easy to spot when they're not being real."

"That's true," Miss Tina says.

I stick up for myself. "I don't know what to say."

I look at Miss Tina for help.

"Guys, the girls have been planning a surprise for you; a secret prom to celebrate the progress you've all made here. They've been making their prom dresses to surprise you."

"I couldn't tell you what was going on or I'd ruin the surprise," I say to Franklin. "You just walked away and then started to ignore me." I shake my head. "It hurt."

"I'm sorry. I like you, okay? And I thought you were going to hurt me like other girls have done in the past."

"What part of yourself were you functioning from, Franklin?" Miss Tina asks him.

He looks downhearted and says, "My negative 'Modified Me.'"

"Yes. Now, let's see how you could have handled it differently. Marsha was asked to keep the secret, and her secretive behavior triggered your memories of when you were hurt, so you assumed the same thing was going to happen again. What you needed to do was to get yourself into your 'Thinking Me' and check it out with Marsha."

She walks to the flipchart and writes, "When you... I feel... And I would like it if you would..." and then she sits back down.

"If you were in your 'Thinking Me' you could have said, 'When you won't give me a straight answer, I feel conned and I lose some trust in you, and

I would like it if you would give me an answer that I can understand, please.' How does that sound?"

"Different than how I handled it," Franklin says honestly.

"Now, how could you have handled it, Marsha? Okay, you had a secret to keep, but you could have said *something* instead of just being secretive. How about, 'I've been asked to keep a secret, but it's nothing horrible.' If you had said something like that, you wouldn't have revealed the secret, but you would have remained honest with Franklin, and he would've felt that you were being real. He'd have felt reassured that you weren't going to hurt him."

"I'm sorry," I say. "I didn't think. I felt a bit hurt, though, that you would think badly of me. I'm not those other girls."

"I'm sorry," he says again. "It's tough to trust again when you've been hurt."

"That's true," Miss Tina says. "But get into your 'Thinking Me' and tell yourself that the girl standing in front of you is not one of those who hurt you."

"Okay," he says sheepishly.

Miss Tina stands up and walks towards some boxes in the corner of the room.

"You have the whole afternoon to get ready for the prom. Guys, your suits are in here," she points to the boxes.

"It's not fair," Leisha moans. "Guys are lucky,

they get to cover their scars beneath a suit, but we girls can't."

Miss Tina taps her head and smiles at her.

"Leisha, have you forgotten that I said I've got a plan? Off you go, now. Go and make yourselves even more beautiful than you already are. I'll meet you girls at seven tonight in the upstairs girls' den, okay? Guys, no peeking!"

"What about our baby-selves? We don't have to wear the slings tonight, do we?" Poppy asks. "It'll ruin our dresses."

Miss Tina smiles and says, "No, of course not, but they have to come to the prom. You can set them on a table, well, not you Greg. You'll have to take care of Little Greg, I'm afraid."

The puppy yaps inside Greg's sling.

"Can we leave them there now so that we can concentrate on getting ready?" Macy asks.

"Well, let's go and sort out the dining room now, and you can put them where you want to." Miss Tina says. "C'mon."

We leave the room noisily. I'm so excited that I feel queasy. Leisha skips down the corridor and she makes me giggle. Her baby-self bounces against her.

The aides are decorating the dining room already and it looks different. The tables have been pushed to the edges of the room, but the big table where our food is served is in the same place. An aide tells us that's where the buffet's going to be. Ken hangs some lights around the room, looking pleased with himself when he switches them on and they twinkle. A DJ is setting up his equipment in the corner of the room, and he tests his mic.

"Where d'you want to put your baby-selves?" Miss Tina asks.

Macy looks around and says, "How about we put them on that table over there?" She points to a table that's half way down the dining room against the wall. "That way they can see," she hardly gets her words out before she cracks up laughing.

Miss Tina laughs with her. "I'm impressed, Macy. You didn't try to stick them in the corner."

Macy stops laughing and cocks her head to one side, like she doesn't understand. "No, why would I? Seeing my baby-self will remind me to have fun from my 'Spontaneous Me.' Besides, I've become really attached to her."

"Good," Miss Tina says. "Okay, I'll see you girls at seven. Have fun all of you." She leaves the room.

Franklin comes over to me. "Marsha, I feel like a jackass."

"Don't. I feel pretty stupid, too."

He looks shy but says, "I can't wait to see your prom dress."

I don't know whether to smile or frown, thinking that I won't look good because of my scars.

"C'mon," Poppy says after she and the other girls

leave their baby-selves on the table. I put Sharsha next to them, and I feel a sudden sense of loss.

"See you later," I say to Franklin, as I follow the girls out of the room.

We head up the spiral staircase towards our rooms and spend hours getting ready. We shower, shave our legs and armpits, put on makeup, curl our hair or straighten it, give up when it goes wrong and start all over again. I peer into the mirror in my bathroom. I swear I can see a spot developing on my chin. Why now? I run to my door and holler down the hall.

"Has anyone got any zit cover-up?"

"Yeah, hang on." Candy comes out of her room with a large towel wrapped around her, and puts it in my hand. "Gotta run, my hair straighteners are ready."

I go back into my bathroom and peer into the mirror. Yes, I swear I can see a zit. I dab the spot cover-up onto my chin and try to blend it in, but when it looks too dark, I scrub my face with soap and water and cuss silently to myself. I start all over again but feel frustrated because now my face is all red. I want to cry. I don't want to go to the prom. It's a silly idea. How can I possibly believe that I could look good in a strappy, backless dress with all my scars? Tears pops into my eyes from nowhere and a lump in my throat threatens to suffocate me. I feel hopeless. What's the point?

I throw myself on my bed and cry.

Leisha stands in my doorway.

"Marsha, what's the matter?"

"I can't do it. My face is a mess. My arms are revolting. My hair won't go right and I've got a zit on my chin," I howl.

"Girl. C'mon. Look at my arms. They look like a tick-tack-toe convention. And look at my hair. Oh, and I couldn't help myself, I squeezed a zit that's been brewing for days. Look!"

I sit up and she tells me to look at the red spot on the tip of her nose. I walk over to her and look. She's squeezed it good and hard, and her nose is redder than my face. I start to laugh as both her eyes converge on her nose. She laughs, too, and we fall into each other's arms, laughing and crying together.

When we pull apart she tells me to get ready, and I do what she says. I start over. I stand under the shower even though I've already had one, and after I towel myself dry, I slip into my underwear. I scrub my teeth really hard and gargle with mouthwash that bites my taste buds but leaves my mouth feeling really clean. I'm glad because I feel so nervous that I swear my breath smells. I wait until the steam clears from the mirror, and when I can see myself, I ignore my red face and put on some makeup. I use a little of Candy's zit cover-up to hide the lump on my chin. Then I curl my hair with a curling iron.

The girls have a CD blaring up the hall and suddenly I feel calmer. I rock my body to the music as I curl my hair. I want to dance.

It feels strange not having Sharsha next to me and I miss her, yet as the music calls at me to dance, I know that I'm in my "Spontaneous Me," so she's still with me.

"What time is it?" Macy asks.

I look at my clock. "It's nearly seven. We'd better hurry because we have to meet Miss Tina at seven."

The hall is deserted as we dive into our rooms to put on our dresses.

Everything seems to be in slow motion as I step into my dress. It fits like a glove, and as I stand in front of the mirror, I can't believe it's me I'm seeing staring back. I stand still, mesmerized, but then a small voice filters into my mind, intent on robbing me. "Don't kid yourself. Look at your arms. You did this. Don't expect anyone to think you look good."

I want to take off my dress, hide in my bed and never come out, but as I think it, Leisha, Macy, Candy and Poppy all stand in my doorway.

"Are you ready?" Macy asks. "C'mon."

I have no choice but to follow them. To refuse would draw more attention to myself and I don't want to do that. I feel awful as I follow the girls along the hall to the girls' den. The girls look awesome, and that makes me feel worse. When they tell me I look fabulous, I block them, believing that they're just saying it to be kind. I sit in a chair not caring if my dress gets creased. I've already given up on the evening.

The girls are talking above each other; they're really excited. I feel full of dread. Even though I'm wearing a beautiful dress and my hair and makeup are pretty good, I feel like dirt. All I can see is my angry criss-cross scars on my forearms. How can I be excited about a prom where I'm going to feel humiliated and ashamed?

Miss Tina breaks into my thoughts as she walks through the door. Miss Cassie follows her.

"Oh my," they say together.

"You all look beautiful."

"Look at your dresses; aren't you proud of your-selves?"

They sit down and suddenly become very serious.

Miss Tina says, "I told you I had a plan. You said that you'd be haunted by what you've done for the rest of your lives. Is that right?"

"Yes," we say, and I mean it. I *am* haunted by what I've done to myself.

"But whether or not you let this take control of your lives is up to you. Yes, you have scars, but people in road accidents have scars and they go on to live wonderful lives. You can, too. Scars will fade, although they won't disappear altogether. What matters is how you perceive what you've done. If you can stay positive, you'll live the wonderful life God intended you to live. Tonight we're having a prom to celebrate the progress you've made here. I'm so proud of you all.

"You can go to the prom feeling positive or negative, which is it going to be? Yes, you have scars on your arms, but when you think positively, you'll be able to get those around you to focus upon the other valuable things about yourself. When you focus upon the negative things, that's all people see."

She looks sad.

"So it's up to you. What are you going to do? Will you be positive or negative? Do you want other people to see you as a positive or negative person?"

"I want to be positive," Poppy says, "but nothing you say will change the fact that I'm ashamed of my scars, and people will judge me when they see them."

"So what can you do?" Miss Tina says. "If you're a positive person, what can you do?"

Poppy shakes her head. I know what she's thinking; people *will* judge us for the scars on our forearms.

"You can either flaunt your scars and be prepared for people to comment on them, which could make you feel bad, or you can disguise them so that people see only your true beauty. It's your choice."

"But how?" I ask.

Miss Cassie stands up and starts to open a box.

She struggles with the tape. We watch and wait. She flicks the mangled tape, that's stuck to her fingers, into the trash.

Miss Cassie says, "I have the perfect way to hide your shame yet to promote your sense of self, your uniqueness, and to make you feel like a million dollars."

I feel alert. I want to feel that way.

Miss Cassie speaks as she opens the box.

"I'm so proud of you for making your beautiful dresses. You all look amazing. I know that each of you is worried about your scars, so what I've done is to make you a pair of dress-gloves. Everyone needs accessories; they *make* an outfit. Wear your beautiful gloves and feel as special as film stars do."

Miss Cassie hands us each a pair of long-sleeved gloves that match our dresses... they're made of the same fabric. I realize that Miss Cassie has made these when we weren't looking. She's awesome.

I slip on my black gloves and stand in front of the mirror in the girls' den. I can't believe what I see. My scars are gone, and I look like a film star. My gloves look like they're meant to be part of my outfit.

Miss Tina's got tears in her eyes. "Oh girls, you look beautiful. I'm so proud of you. C'mon, let's go. The guys are waiting for you at the bottom of the stairs."

Leisha grabs my hand, and an excited squeak

escapes from her as we follow Miss Tina and Miss Cassie. At the top of the stairs, Miss Cassie tells us to wait while Miss Tina goes ahead. We can hear her.

"Gentlemen, may I present the beautiful ladies of Beach Haven."

Miss Cassie nudges Macy, telling her to go down the stairs, and we all follow her. My stomach's in shreds but I feel amazing.

As we turn the corner, I gasp. The whole reception area is full of people. The guys, who are at the foot of the stairs, start hooting and hollering, and everyone starts clapping. I see Mom and Dad, and they're clapping really hard. Tears spring into my eyes.

As I walk towards them, Franklin tries to catch up with me.

"Mom, Dad, I didn't know you were coming," I say, giving them both a hug.

Dad laughs, "Ah, we were sworn to secrecy."

"Me, too," I say as Franklin reaches my side. I introduce him to my parents and he shakes their hands politely.

"Come and meet my parents," he says, and we head through the crowd towards a group of people. He introduces us to his parents, grandparents and four older brothers. As his dad asks mine about losing his legs in Iraq, and our moms talk about my dress, Franklin slips his hand into mine, and whispers,

"Let's go," into my ear.

We walk along the corridor hand in hand, and he tells me how beautiful I am. I tell him he looks cool in his suit and bow tie. We head towards the dining room where music is blaring out.

As we step into the room he leads me towards the table where our baby-selves lean against each other; they look hilarious. I wonder what our families will think of them. They might think them odd, but I don't care. Franklin picks Frankie up and hands him to me, and then picks Sharsha up. He sets her down at the end of the line of baby-selves and then takes Frankie from me. He puts him next to Sharsha and positions their arms around each other. He makes me giggle; they look so funny but I know what he's trying to tell me.

He takes my hand and leads me into the middle of the room. And even though he's shy and no one's dancing yet, he puts his hands on my waist and I wrap my arms around his neck. We sway from side to side in time to the music, and I feel the warmth of his cheek on mine as he whispers in my ear, "Marsha, you're beautiful inside and out."

"So are you," I breathe, as the giddy feeling of true intimacy washes over me once more.

About the Author

Dr. Celia Banting earned her Ph.D. by studying suicide attempts in adolescents and developing a risk assessment tool to identify those young people who may be at risk of attempting suicide. She identified several risk factors which, when combined, could increase the likelihood of  an individual attempting suicide. Rather than write "how to" books or text books to help teenagers cope with the risk factors, Dr. Banting has incorporated therapeutic interventions into novels that adolescents will be able to identify with. These novels are designed to increase the adolescents' ability to take care of themselves, should they have minimal support in their families.

Dr. Banting's career has revolved around caring for children in a variety of settings in both the United Kingdom and the United States. She is dedicated to helping troubled children avoid the extreme act of suicide.

WIGHITA PRESS ORDER FORM

Book Title	Price	Qty.	Total

I Only Said I Had No Choice
ISBN 0-9786648-0-9 $14.99 x _____ $ _____
  Shane learns how to control his anger and make positive life
  choices; and he gains understanding about adult co-dependency.

I Only Said "Yes" So That They'd Like Me
ISBN 0-9786648-1-7 $14.99 x _____ $ _____
  Melody learns how to cope with being bullied by the in-crowd
  at school and explores the emotional consequences of casual
  sex. She raises her self-esteem and learns what true beauty is.

I Only Said I Couldn't Cope
ISBN 0-9786648-2-5 $14.99 x _____ $ _____
  Adam learns how to deal with grief and depression. He works
  through the grieving process and explores his perceptions of
  death and life.

I Only Said I Didn't Want You Because I Was Terrified
ISBN 0-9786648-3-3 $14.99 x _____ $ _____
  Hannah experiences peer pressure to drink alcohol. She learns
  about teenage pregnancy, birth, and caring for a new baby.
  Hannah faces the consequences of telling lies and learns how to
  repair broken trust.

I Only Said I Was Telling the Truth
ISBN 0-9786648-4-1 $14.99 x _____ $ _____
  Ruby embarks upon a journey to rid herself of the damaging
  emotional consequences of sexual abuse.

I Only Said I Could Handle It, But I Was Wrong
ISBN 9780978664855 $14.99 x _____ $ _____
  Simon embarks upon the most challenging journey of his
  life—to give up drugs, understand why he takes them and
  reclaim his life.

I Only Said It Didn't Hurt
ISBN 9780978664862 $14.99 x _____ $ _____
  Marsha cuts herself. As she learns how to cope with stress
  safely, she discovers a secret about herself that makes it
  impossible to ever cut again.

I Only Said I Wasn't Hungry
ISBN 9780978664879 $14.99 x _____ $ _____
  Ellie is bullied about her weight and sees food as her
  enemy. She learns to resist the voice of anorexia and explores
  the reasons for her poor self-image.

continued on reverse

WIGHITA PRESS ORDER FORM

Book Title	Price	Qty.	Total

I Only Said I Wanted to Kill Myself;
I Didn't Really Mean It
ISBN 9780978664886 $14.99   x _____ $ _____

     Kenny is angry and hates authority figures, but he forms
     a relationship with Miss Tina who teaches him how to
     get his needs met without acting up. He eventually understands
     why adults have to set rules.

I Only Said Leave Me Out of It
ISBN 9780978664893 $14.99   x _____ $ _____

     Maizy's parents divorce and she learns that, although
     it hurts when others are unkind or unjust, everyone has
     a choice as to how to respond. She finds a valued place
     in her new blended family.

Sub Total $_____

Sales Tax 7.5% ($1.13 per book) $_____

Shipping/handling $_____

1st book, $2.50; each add'l. book $1.00 / U.S. orders only.
(For orders outside the United States, contact Wighita Press.)

TOTAL DUE $_____

PLEASE PRINT ALL INFORMATION.

Customer name: _____

Mailing address: _____

City/State/Zip: _____

Phone Number(s): _____

E-mail address: _____

Make check or money order payable to Wighita Press and

mail order to: P.O. Box 30399, Little Rock, Arkansas 72260-0399

✦ ✦ ✦

Look for us on the web at: www.wighitapress.com

(501) 455-0905 or after office hours: (501) 952-1321